D1131505

ORTHOGONAL FAMILIES OF ANALYTIC FUNCTIONS

ORTHOGONAL
FAMILIES
OF
ANALYTIC
FUNCTIONS

3^3

BERNARD EPSTEIN *of the University of New Mexico and the Office of Naval Research*

The Macmillan Company, New York   Collier-Macmillan Limited, London

First Printing

Library of Congress catalog card number: 65–14070

THE MACMILLAN COMPANY, NEW YORK
COLLIER-MACMILLAN CANADA, LTD., TORONTO, ONTARIO

PRINTED IN THE UNITED STATES OF AMERICA

Preface

The theory of orthogonal families of analytic functions, or, more generally, of function spaces possessing a reproducing kernel, is one of great elegance. Furthermore, it has proved to be a powerful tool of investigation in various branches of analysis, such as conformal mapping and boundary-value problems of the elliptic type. In writing this brief tract it has been my purpose to provide an introduction to the substantial literature that has come into existence since the pioneering work of S. Bergman, S. Bochner, and G. Szegö in the early 1920's. Although a number of excellent books on this subject have appeared, I believe that there is a need for a simple presentation that will serve to interest the newcomer and to smooth his way into the more advanced works and the research literature. It is my hope that I have succeeded to some extent in satisfying this need.

The basic prerequisites have been kept as modest as possible—a knowledge of the elements of linear algebra and of the theory of analytic functions. When it has been necessary to refer to topics not ordinarily covered in introductory courses in the above subjects, an attempt has been made to treat these topics in a way that will minimize the difficulty for the reader who is unacquainted with them.

I first learned of the existence of this beautiful subject through personal contact with Stefan Bergman, who has contributed so much and so profoundly to its development. It is appropriate to express publicly to him, on this occasion, my appreciation and respect.

I am deeply grateful to Dr. John Dettman for checking the galley proofs when serious illness prevented me from attending to this task. He performed this work with great competence, and on very short notice. I was able to check the page proofs, and all responsibility for any oversights is mine alone.

BERNARD EPSTEIN

London, England

Contents

ORTHOGONAL FAMILIES OF ANALYTIC FUNCTIONS

1

The Space $\mathfrak{L}_2(D)$

¶ **1-1** Let D denote any bounded* domain of the x, y-plane, and let $f(x, y)$ and $g(x, y)$ be any two continuous, but not necessarily bounded, complex-valued functions for which the integrals

$$\int\int_D |f|^2 \, dx \, dy \quad \text{and} \quad \int\int_D |g|^2 \, dx \, dy$$

both exist.† From the inequality $|f + g|^2 \leqslant 2|f|^2 + 2|g|^2$ (which follows from the equality $|f + g|^2 + |f - g|^2 = 2|f|^2 + 2|g|^2$) it then follows that the integral $\int\int_D |f + g|^2 \, dx \, dy$ also exists. Since the existence of the first two integrals evidently assures the existence of of the integrals $\int\int_D |\lambda f|^2 \, dx \, dy$ and $\int\int_D |\mu g|^2 \, dx \, dy$, where λ and μ are arbitrary complex numbers, it follows more generally that the

---

* The restriction of boundedness is made for the sake of simplicity; all arguments to be presented in the present chapter and in the following chapters are valid, with at most minor modifications, for an unbounded domain whose boundary contains at least one component consisting of more than a single point.

† "Existence" is always understood to imply that the integral possesses a *finite* value.

integral $\int\int_D |\lambda f + \mu g|^2 \, dx \, dy$ also exists. Furthermore, from the inequality $|f\bar{g}| \leqslant \frac{1}{2}|f|^2 + \frac{1}{2}|g|^2$ [which is an immediate consequence of the equality $|f|^2 - 2|f\bar{g}| + |g|^2 = (|f| - |g|)^2$] we observe that the integral $\int\int_D [\frac{1}{2}|f|^2 + \frac{1}{2}|g|^2] \, dx \, dy$ dominates the integral $\int\int_D f\bar{g} \, dx \, dy$, and hence the latter exists.

If we denote the integral $\int\int_D f\bar{g} \, dx \, dy$ by the symbol (f, g) and the nonnegative real number $(f, f)^{1/2}$ by the symbol $\|f\|$, we may summarize the above paragraph by asserting that the existence of $\|f\|$ and $\|g\|$ implies the existence of $\|\lambda f + \mu g\|$ and of (f, g). Furthermore, the quantity $\|f\|$ is positive except in the trivial case when f vanishes identically, for, if f differs from 0 at some point P of D, then $|f|^2$ must be positive in some neighborhood Δ of P (since f is assumed continuous); therefore $\|f\|^2 \geqslant \int\int_\Delta |f|^2 \, dx \, dy > 0$.

¶ **1-2** If the function f is analytic in the complex variable $z = x + iy$ and if t denotes a fixed point of D, then the value of $\|f\|$ immediately provides an upper bound on $|f(t)|$. This bound is obtained by the following simple argument: Let C denote the circle $|z - t| = r$, where r is so small that C and its interior are contained in D. Then the Cauchy integral formula, when applied to the analytic function $f^2(z)$ and the contour C, furnishes the equality

$$f^2(t) = \frac{1}{2\pi} \int_0^{2\pi} f^2(t + re^{i\theta}) \, d\theta. \tag{1-1}$$

Multiplying both sides of (1-1) by $r \, dr$ and integrating from 0 to R, where R denotes the distance from t to the boundary of D, we obtain

$$\tfrac{1}{2}R^2 f^2(t) = \frac{1}{2\pi} \int_0^{2\pi} \int_0^R f^2(t + re^{i\theta}) r \, dr \, d\theta = \frac{1}{2\pi} \int\int_{|z-t|<R} f^2(z) \, dx \, dy, \tag{1-2}$$

and hence

$$\pi R^2 |f(t)|^2 \leqslant \int\int_{|z-t|<R} |f|^2 \, dx \, dy \leqslant \int\int_D |f|^2 \, dx \, dy = \|f\|^2. \tag{1-3}$$

Thus, we obtain the desired inequality,

$$|f(t)| \leqslant c(t)\|f\|, \qquad c(t) = (\pi R^2)^{-1/2}. \tag{1-4}$$

Now suppose that a sequence $f_1(z), f_2(z), \ldots$ of analytic functions is given such that $\lim\limits_{m,\,n \to \infty} \|f_m - f_n\| = 0$—i.e., for any given positive number ϵ there exists an integer N such that $\|f_m - f_n\| < \epsilon$ whenever

m and n both exceed N. Given a point t in D and any positive number δ, let N be chosen corresponding to the quantity $\epsilon = \delta/c(t)$. Replacing f in (1-4) by $f_m - f_n$, we find that the inequality

$$|f_m(t) - f_n(t)| < \delta \qquad (1\text{-}5)$$

holds whenever m and n both exceed N; therefore, it follows that the given sequence of functions converges at t, and hence throughout D. Furthermore, if t is restricted to a compact subset D' of D, the quantity $c(t)$ possesses a positive lower bound c'. Therefore, if ϵ is defined as δ/c' and N is chosen accordingly, it follows that the inequality (1-5) holds throughout D' whenever m and n exceed the *fixed* (i.e., independent of t) index N. Thus, we have shown that the given sequence of functions converges "regularly" (uniformly in every compact subset) in D, and it then follows from one of the basic theorems of the theory of analytic functions that the limit of the sequence, which we denote by $f(z)$, is also analytic in D. It is to be expected that the integral $\iint_D |f|^2\, dx\, dy$ exists and that

$$\lim_{n \to \infty} \|f - f_n\| = 0.$$

The two assertions are, in fact, correct, and their proofs will be given in Section 1-4.

Henceforth, the symbol $C_2(D)$ will denote the family of all continuous functions $f(z)$ such that $\|f\|$ exists, and $\mathscr{L}_2(D)$ will denote the subset of $C_2(D)$ consisting of those functions that are analytic.

PROBLEMS

1-1. Let $f_n(z) = nz^n$ and let $f(z) \equiv 0$. Prove that the sequence $\{f_n(z)\}$ converges regularly to $f(z)$ in the unit disc ($|z| < 1$) but that neither of the limiting relationships $\lim\limits_{m,\, n \to \infty} \|f_m - f_n\| = 0$, $\lim\limits_{n \to \infty} \|f - f_n\| = 0$ is satisfied.

1-2. Let $f_n(z) = (1 - z^n)/(1 - z)$, let $f(z) = 1/(1 - z)$, and let D be the unit disc. Prove that each function $f_n(z)$ belongs to $\mathscr{L}_2(D)$ and that the sequence $\{f_n(z)\}$ converges regularly in D to $f(z)$, but that $f(z)$ does not belong to $\mathscr{L}_2(D)$.

¶ **1-3** In this section we shall prove two important inequalities. First, let $f(x, y)$ and $g(x, y)$ denote any two functions belonging to the family $C_2(D)$, and consider the quantity $\|f + , g\|^2$, or $(f + \lambda g, f + \lambda g)$, as a function of the real variable λ. On the one hand this expression works out to $\|f\|^2 + 2\lambda \,\mathrm{Re}\,(f, g) + \lambda^2\|g\|^2$, and on the other hand it can assume only real nonnegative values. From elementary algebra we then conclude that the discriminant of this quadratic expression must be nonpositive, and so we obtain the inequality

$$[\mathrm{Re}\,(f, g)]^2 \leqslant \|f\|^2 \cdot \|g\|^2,$$

or

$$|\mathrm{Re}\,(f, g)| \leqslant \|f\| \cdot \|g\|. \tag{1-6}$$

If we replace f by μf, where μ denotes an arbitrary complex number of unit modulus, we obtain the more general inequality

$$|\mathrm{Re}\,\mu(f, g)| \leqslant \|f\| \cdot \|g\| \tag{1-7}$$

(since $\|\mu f\| = \|f\|$). Now we choose μ so that $\mu(f, g)$ is real and non-negative, and, therefore, equal to its own absolute value. Then (1-7) assumes the form $|\mu(f, g)| \leqslant \|f\| \cdot \|g\|$. Since $|\mu(f, g)| = |\mu| \cdot |(f, g)| = |(f, g)|$, we obtain the "Schwarz inequality"

$$|(f, g)| \leqslant \|f\| \cdot \|g\|. \tag{1-8}$$

From the manner in which (1-8) was derived it is readily seen that the two sides are equal if and only if there exists a number α, not necessarily real, such that $f(x, y) + \alpha g(x, y) \equiv 0$; an exception occurs in the trivial case $g(x, y) \equiv 0$, in which case equality holds in (1-8) for any function $f(x, y)$. This exceptional case can be circumvented by reformulating the above condition in the following slightly different form: Equality holds in (1-8) if and only if there exist two numbers α_1 and α_2, at least one of which is different from 0, such that $\alpha_1 f(x, y) + \alpha_2 g(x, y) \equiv 0$.

From the equality $\|f + g\|^2 = \|f\|^2 + 2\,\mathrm{Re}\,(f, g) + \|g\|^2$ we immediately obtain the *inequality* $\|f + g\|^2 \leqslant \|f\|^2 + 2|(f, g)| + \|g\|^2$, and from (1-8) we now obtain

$$\|f + g\|^2 \leqslant \|f\|^2 + 2\|f\| \cdot \|g\| + \|g\|^2 = (\|f\| + \|g\|)^2. \tag{1-9}$$

Taking the (nonnegative) square root of each side, we obtain the "triangle inequality"

$$\|f + g\| \leqslant \|f\| + \|g\|. \tag{1-10}$$

Equality holds in (1-10) if and only if $\mathrm{Re}\,(f, g) = |(f, g)| = \|f\| \cdot \|g\|$, and from the manner in which (1-8) was derived it is evident that the foregoing pair of equalities hold if and only if $f(x, y)$ and $g(x, y)$ are real positive multiples of each other (except for the trivial case when at least one of these two functions vanishes identically).

¶ **1-4** Since $\mathscr{L}_2(D)$ is a subset of $C_2(D)$, the inequalities (1-8) and (1-10) hold in $\mathscr{L}_2(D)$. We shall now use these inequalities to prove the assertions made at the end of Section 1-2 concerning the existence of $\|f\|$ and the limiting relationship $\lim\limits_{n \to \infty} \|f - f_n\| = 0$. First we replace f and g in (1-10) by f_n and $(f_m - f_n)$, respectively, and thus obtain $\|f_m\| \leqslant \|f_n\| + \|f_m - f_n\|$, or $\|f_m\| - \|f_n\| \leqslant \|f_m - f_n\|$. Interchanging the indices m and n in the latter inequality, we obtain

$$\|f_n\| - \|f_m\| \leqslant \|f_n - f_m\| = \|f_m - f_n\|,$$

or $\|f_m\| - \|f_n\| \geqslant -\|f_m - f_n\|$. Thus, we have obtained the pair of inequalities $-\|f_m - f_n\| \leqslant \|f_m\| - \|f_n\| \leqslant \|f_m - f_n\|$, which can be condensed into the single inequality

$$\big| \, \|f_m\| - \|f_n\| \, \big| \leqslant \|f_m - f_n\|. \tag{1-11}$$

Therefore, whenever $\lim\limits_{m,\,n \to \infty} \|f_m - f_n\| = 0$, the quantities $\|f_1\|$, $\|f_2\|, \ldots$ form a sequence of real numbers satisfying the Cauchy criterion. This sequence is, therefore, convergent and, *a fortiori*, bounded.

Returning to the sequence of analytic functions considered in Section 1-2, we can now assert that the quantities $\int\int_D |f_n|^2 \, dx \, dy$ are bounded by some fixed number, say, M. If D' denotes any compact subset of D, it then follows that the inequality

$$\int\int_{D'} |f_n|^2 \, dx \, dy \leqslant M \tag{1-12}$$

holds for each index n. Since the sequence $\{f_n(z)\}$ converges *uniformly* in D' to the limit function $f(z)$, it follows that

$$\int\int_{D'} |f|^2 \, dx \, dy \leqslant M. \tag{1-13}$$

Since M is independent of D', it follows that (1-13) must hold when D' is replaced by the entire domain D. Thus, we have established the existence of $\|f\|$.

It is now meaningful to speak of $\|f - f_n\|$. In order to show that this quantity approaches 0 with increasing n, let ϵ denote any positive number, let $N(\epsilon)$ be chosen as in Section 1-2, and then let D be divided into a compact subset D' and a remaining portion D'' such that $\|f\|'' < \epsilon$ and $\|f_{N+1}\|'' < \epsilon$, where $\| \ \|''$, in analogy with

$\| \ \|$, implies integration over D''. (Similarly, $\| \ \|'$ implies integration over D'.) Now $\|f - f_n\|^2 = \|f - f_n\|'^2 + \|f - f_n\|''^2$. Since

$$\begin{aligned}
\|f - f_n\|'' &= \|f + (f_{N+1} - f_n) + (-f_{N+1}\|'' \\
&\leqslant \|f\|'' + \|f_{N+1} - f_n\|'' + \|f_{N+1}\|'' \\
&< \epsilon + \|f_{N+1} - f_n\| + \epsilon,
\end{aligned}$$

we obtain for all indices n exceeding N the inequality $\|f - f_n\|'' < 3\epsilon$. Thus

$$\|f - f_n\|^2 < \|f - f_n\|'^2 + 9\epsilon^2. \tag{1-14}$$

Since the functions $\{f_n(z)\}$ converge uniformly to $f(z)$ in D', so that $\|f - f_n\|' \to 0$, we obtain

$$\limsup_{n \to \infty} \|f - f_n\|^2 \leqslant 9\epsilon^2. \tag{1-15}$$

Since ϵ was arbitrary, we conclude that $\lim_{n \to \infty} \|f - f_n\|$ exists and equals 0. Finally, replacing f_m in (1-11) by f, we conclude that $\lim_{n \to \infty} \|f_n\|$ exists and is equal to $\|f\|$.

PROBLEMS

1-3. Prove that if the functions $\{f_n(z)\}$ belong to $\mathscr{L}_2(D)$ and converge regularly to $f(z)$, then $\|f\| \leqslant \liminf_{n \to \infty} \|f_n\|$. (If $\|f\|$ does not exist, this inequality implies that the sequence $\{\|f_n\|\}$ contains no bounded subsequence.)

1-4. Prove by means of simple examples that in $C_2(D)$, in contrast to $\mathscr{L}_2(D)$, the limiting relation $\lim_{m,n \to \infty} \|f_m - f_n\| = 0$ implies *neither* of the following:

(a) Convergence of the sequence $\{f_n(x, y)\}$ at all points (or even at *any* point) of D.

(b) The existence of a function $f(x, y)$ belonging to $C_2(D)$ such that $\lim_{n \to \infty} \|f - f_n\| = 0$.

2

Hilbert Spaces

¶ **2-1** The derivations of the Schwarz inequality (1-8) and of the triangle inequality (1-10) in Chapter 1 do not actually depend on the fact that the expression (f, g) denotes a certain integral—namely, $\int\int_D f\bar{g}\,dx\,dy$. Rather, they depend only on the validity [for every complex number λ and all functions f, g, h belonging to $C_2(D)$] of the equations

$$(\lambda f, g) = \lambda(f, g), \tag{2-1}$$

$$(f + g, h) = (f, h) + (g, h), \tag{2-2}$$

and
$$(f, g) = \overline{(g, f)}, \tag{2-3}$$

and on the fact that the inequality

$$(f, f) \geqslant 0 \tag{2-4}$$

always holds. This observation suggests that the Schwarz and triangle inequalities, and presumably other interesting theorems, can be formulated in a much more general setting than that which was employed in Chapter 1. The appropriate setting is, in fact, an "inner-product space." By this term we mean a complex linear space together with a function (,) which assigns to every *ordered* pair of vectors in the space a complex number; the inner product (,) is required to satisfy the equalities (2-1), (2-2), (2-3), and also the following modified version of (2-4):

$$ \cdot (f,f) > 0, \tag{2-4'} $$

for every vector f other than the zero vector θ. [Since, by (2-1), $(\theta, g) = (0g, g) = 0(g, g) = 0$, it follows that $(\theta, \theta) = 0$; it also follows immediately from (2-3) that (f, f) must be real.] The condition (2-4') enables us to define the "norm" of every nonzero vector f, denoted $\|f\|$, as the positive square root of (f,f); the norm of the vector θ is, of course, defined to be 0. A simple computation based on (2-1) and (2-3) furnishes the homogeneity property

$$ \|\lambda f\| = |\lambda| \cdot \|f\|. \tag{2-5} $$

It is now immediately evident that the arguments employed in Chapter 1 apply equally well in any inner-product space, and so we may consider the Schwarz inequality

$$ |(f, g)| \leqslant \|f\| \cdot \|g\| \tag{2-6} $$

and the triangle inequality

$$ \|f + g\| \leqslant \|f\| + \|g\| \tag{2-7} $$

as established. Furthermore, the conditions that equality should hold in (2-6) or (2-7) are straightforward generalizations of those stated in Chapter 1.

PROBLEMS

2-1. Prove (2-5).

2-2. Prove, by defining a suitable inner-product space, the Cauchy-Schwarz inequality

$$ \left| \sum_{k=1}^{n} \alpha_k \bar{\beta}_k \right|^2 \leqslant \left(\sum_{k=1}^{n} |\alpha_k|^2 \right) \left(\sum_{k=1}^{n} |\beta_k|^2 \right) \tag{2-8} $$

for any $2n$ complex numbers $\alpha_1, \alpha_2, \ldots, \alpha_n, \beta_1, \beta_2, \ldots, \beta_n$.

¶ **2-2** The introduction of the norm enables us to define a distance between any two vectors, f and g, as follows:

$$ \rho(f, g) = \|f - g\|. \tag{2-9} $$

It is readily seen from this definition that

$$\rho(f,f) = 0,$$
$$\rho(f,g) > 0 \quad \text{if} \quad f \neq g, \Bigg\} \tag{2-10}$$

and
$$\rho(f,g) = \rho(g,f). \tag{2-11}$$

Also, from the triangle inequality (2-7) we easily obtain

$$\rho(f,h) \leqslant \rho(f,g) + \rho(g,h). \tag{2-12}$$

This inequality, like (2-7), is also termed the triangle inequality. (The reader is probably acquainted with the fact that (2-10), (2-11), and (2-12) are the axioms for a metric space.)

The introduction of the concept of distance makes it possible to define convergence in an inner-product space in a manner similar to that employed in real analysis. Given a set S of vectors, the vector f (not necessarily contained in S) is termed a "limit point" of S if for every positive number ϵ there exist infinitely many vectors contained in S whose distance from f is less than ϵ. A sequence of vectors $f_1, f_2, \ldots$ is said to converge to the vector f if for every positive number ϵ there exists an integer N such that $\|f - f_n\| < \epsilon$ whenever $n > N$. Exactly as in real analysis, one can show that a sequence cannot have more than one limit, and that f is a limit point of a set S if and only if it is possible to extract a sequence $f_1, f_2, \ldots$ of *distinct* vectors from S that converges to f. A set is said to be closed if it contains all its limit points, and it is said to be open if its complement is closed.

If the sequence $f_1, f_2, \ldots$ is convergent, then for every positive number ϵ there exists an integer N such that the inequality

$$\|f_n - f_m\| < \epsilon \tag{2-13}$$

holds whenever m and n exceed N. For, if f is the (necessarily unique) limit of the sequence, we simply choose N so large that

$$\|f - f_p\| < \frac{\epsilon}{2} \tag{2-14}$$

whenever $p > N$; then, if both m and n exceed N, we obtain

$$\|f_n - f_m\| = \|(f_n - f) + (f - f_m)\|$$
$$\leqslant \|f - f_n\| + \|f - f_n\| < \frac{\epsilon}{2} + \frac{\epsilon}{2} = \epsilon. \tag{2-15}$$

A fact of fundamental importance in real analysis is given by the converse of the above assertion. A sequence of real numbers $x_1, x_2, \ldots$ is said to be a "Cauchy sequence" if for every positive number ϵ there exists a positive integer N such that the inequality

$$|x_m - x_n| < \epsilon \qquad (2\text{-}16)$$

holds whenever m and n exceed N. The Cauchy criterion asserts that a Cauchy sequence of real numbers is convergent.

Although the Cauchy criterion extends beyond the real number system (cf. Problem 2-5), it does not hold in all inner-product spaces. An inner-product space in which the Cauchy criterion holds is called a "Hilbert space."

The concept of a Cauchy sequence is applicable to any metric space: A Cauchy sequence is defined to be a sequence of points, say $\xi_1, \xi_2, \ldots$, such that for every positive number ϵ there exists an integer N such that $\rho(\xi_m, \xi_n) < \epsilon$ whenever m and n exceed N. A metric space is said to be "complete" if every Cauchy sequence is convergent, in the sense that there exists a (necessarily unique) point ξ in the space such that $\rho(\xi, \xi_n)$ approaches 0 as n increases. A Hilbert space is, therefore, an inner-product space that is complete when considered as a metric space with the distance-function defined by (2-9).

According to Problem 2-9, every finite-dimensional inner-product space is complete. Also, the reasoning employed in Section 1-3 shows that $\mathscr{L}_2(D)$ is complete, whereas $C_2(D)$ is, according to Problem 2-4, not complete. Thus, $\mathscr{L}_2(D)$ furnishes an example of an infinite-dimensional* Hilbert space. (The term "Hilbert space" is often understood to imply infinite dimensionality.) Another important example of an infinite-dimensional Hilbert space is the space l_2 consisting of all sequences $\{\alpha_1, \alpha_2, \ldots\}$ of complex numbers satisfying the restriction that the infinite series $\sum\limits_{k=1}^{\infty} |\alpha_k|^2$ converges, the inner product of two vectors, say $a = \{\alpha_1, \alpha_2, \ldots\}$ and $b = \{\beta_1, \beta_2, \ldots\}$, being given by

$$(a, b) = \sum_{k=1}^{\infty} \alpha_k \bar{\beta}_k. \qquad (2\text{-}17)$$

The proof that l_2 satisfies all the axioms of a Hilbert space is left as Problem 2-5.

---

* The functions $1, z, z^2, \ldots$ are linearly independent and belong to $\mathscr{L}_2(D)$, so that the latter cannot be finite-dimensional.

PROBLEMS

2-3. Prove (2-10), (2-11), and (2-12).

2-4. Show that the inner-product space $C_2(D)$ defined in Chapter 1 is not complete by exhibiting a Cauchy sequence that does not converge.

2-5. Prove in detail that l_2 is a Hilbert space; in particular, it must be shown that the definition (2-17) of the inner product is meaningful.

¶ **2-3** Although much of what is to be said in the remainder of this chapter is valid in any inner-product space, the completeness property is essential at certain points. Therefore, we shall always have a Hilbert space, to be denoted $\mathscr{H}$, in mind.

Two vectors, f and g, are said to be "orthogonal," or "perpendicular," if the inner product (f, g) vanishes. Since $(f, g) = \overline{(g, f)}$, the orthogonality relationship is a symmetric one. Also, since

$$(\alpha_1 f_1 + \alpha_2 f_2, g) = \alpha_1(f_1, g) + \alpha_2(f_2, g),$$

it follows that if f_1 and f_2 are each orthogonal to g, then so is any linear combination of these two vectors; by induction, this assertion generalizes to any finite number of vectors $f_1, f_2, \ldots, f_n$. Furthermore, if the sequence $f_1, f_2, \ldots$ converges to f and if each vector of the sequence is orthogonal to g, then f is also orthogonal to g; for $(f, g) = (f - f_n, g) + (f_n, g) = (f - f_n, g)$, and so, by the Schwarz inequality, $|(f, g)| \leqslant \|f - f_n\| \cdot \|g\| \to 0$. Thus, the set of all vectors orthogonal to a given vector is a *closed* linear manifold*; the same assertion is true, more generally, for the set of vectors orthogonal to *every* vector of a given nonempty subset S of $\mathscr{H}$. This set is called the "orthogonal complement" of S and is denoted $S^\perp$.

A simple calculation shows that if f and g are orthogonal, the equality

$$\|f + g\|^2 = \|f\|^2 + \|g\|^2 \tag{2-18}$$

is satisfied. This result, which for obvious reasons is sometimes called the "Pythagorean theorem," evidently extends to any finite set of vectors that are orthogonal by pairs.

A collection S of vectors is said to be "orthonormal" if the norm of each vector in S is equal to 1 and if any two distinct vectors in S are orthogonal. Any finite orthonormal set of vectors $\{e_1, e_2, \ldots, e_n\}$ is linearly independent, for if we write

$$\alpha_1 e_1 + \alpha_2 e_2 + \cdots + \alpha_n e_n = \theta, \tag{2-19}$$

---

* A closed linear manifold is sometimes called a subspace.

and take the inner product of each side of (2-19) with itself, we obtain, by the Pythagorean theorem,

$$|\alpha_1|^2 + |\alpha_2|^2 + \cdots + |\alpha_n|^2 = 0, \qquad (2\text{-}20)$$

and so $\alpha_1 = \alpha_2 = \cdots = \alpha_n = 0$.

Every finite-dimensional inner-product space possesses an orthonormal basis. This important fact is demonstrated by selecting an arbitrary basis $\{f_1, f_2, \ldots, f_n\}$ and carrying out the "Gram–Schmidt" orthonormalization procedure, which we sketch as follows, leaving detailed justification for Problem 2-7. Since $f_1 \neq \theta$ (otherwise f_1 could not be part of a basis), we may define e_1 to be the vector $\|f_1\|^{-1}f_1$. Then we choose the scalar α such that $f_2 - \alpha f_1$ is orthogonal to e_1; this condition uniquely determines α, and the vector $f_2 - \alpha f_1$ is different from θ, so that we may define e_2 as $\|f_2 - \alpha f_1\|^{-1}(f_2 - \alpha f_1)$. Similarly, we choose scalars β and γ such that $f_3 - \beta f_1 - \gamma f_2$ is orthogonal to e_1 and to e_2, and then define e_3 to be the vector $\|f_3 - \beta f_1 - \gamma f_2\|^{-1}(f_3 - \beta f_1 - \gamma f_2)$. Continuing in this way, we obtain an orthonormal set $\{e_1, e_2, \ldots, e_n\}$ which, like the set $\{f_1, f_2, \ldots, f_n\}$, is a basis.

A simple computation shows that, in terms of the orthonormal basis $e_1, e_2, \ldots, e_n$, each vector f in a finite-dimensional inner-product space possesses the representation

$$f = \sum_{k=1}^{n} (f, e_k)e_k. \qquad (2\text{-}21)$$

Also, another simple computation furnishes the equality

$$\|f\|^2 = \sum_{k=1}^{n} |(f, e_k)|^2. \qquad (2\text{-}22)$$

Turning to the case when $\mathscr{H}$ is infinite-dimensional, we find it convenient to define a basis as a linearly independent collection of vectors S such that every vector in $\mathscr{H}$ can be approximated arbitrarily closely by a finite linear combination of vectors in S. By this we mean that, given any vector f in $\mathscr{H}$ and any positive number ϵ, there exist vectors $f_1, f_2, \ldots, f_n$ belonging to S and scalars $\alpha_1, \alpha_2, \ldots, \alpha_n$ such that

$$\|f - (\alpha_1 f_1 + \alpha_2 f_2 + \cdots + \alpha_n f_n)\| < \epsilon. \qquad (2\text{-}23)$$

(The number of vectors, n, and the set of vectors $\{f_1, f_2, \ldots, f_n\}$ are not preassigned.) The argument employed in the previous paragraph to show that every finite-dimensional inner-product space possesses an orthonormal basis is easily seen to extend to the case when $\mathscr{H}$ is "separable"; we say that $\mathscr{H}$ is separable if it possesses a denumerable subset $\{f_1, f_2, \ldots\}$ such that, for every vector f in $\mathscr{H}$ and every positive number ϵ, there exists a vector f_k in this subset such that the inequality

$$\|f - f_k\| < \epsilon \qquad (2\text{-}24)$$

holds. Briefly, one selects such a denumerable subset, eliminates each vector (if any) in the subset that is expressible as a linear combination of its predecessors, and carries out the Gram-Schmidt procedure with the set of vectors that have not been eliminated. The details of the argument are left as Problem 2-8. (If $\mathscr{H}$ is not separable, the existence of an orthonormal basis may be demonstrated by transfinite induction.) In particular, we mention the fact, which will be proved in Section 3-4, that $\mathscr{L}_2(D)$ is separable, and, hence, possesses a denumerable orthonormal basis.

Finally, we remark that the converse of the above result holds: A Hilbert space with a denumerable basis is separable. The proof is left as Problem 2-11.

PROBLEMS

2-6. Prove that, for any nonempty set S, the set $(S^{\perp})^{\perp}$ is the smallest closed linear manifold that contains S.

2-7. Carry out the detailed justification of the Gram-Schmidt procedure.

2-8. Carry out in detail the proof of the existence of an orthonormal basis of an infinite-dimensional separable Hilbert space.

2-9. Prove, with the aid of an orthonormal basis, that every finite-dimensional inner-product space is complete.

2-10. Let $\tilde{l}_2$ denote the subset of l_2 consisting of those sequences possessing only a finite number of nonzero terms. Prove that $\tilde{l}_2$ is not complete.

2-11. Prove the assertion made in the final paragraph of Section 2-3.

¶ **2-4** Let the vectors $e_1, e_2, \ldots, e_n$ be a finite orthonormal set in $\mathscr{H}$, let f be any vector, let $\alpha_k = (f, e_k)$, and let the scalars β_k be chosen arbitrarily. A simple computation (Problem 2-12) furnishes the equality

$$\left\| f - \sum_{k=1}^{n} \beta_k e_k \right\|^2 = \|f\|^2 - \sum_{k=1}^{n} |\alpha_k|^2 + \sum_{k=1}^{n} |\beta_k - \alpha_k|^2. \qquad (2\text{-}25)$$

Thus, the left side of (2-25) is minimized by choosing for β_k the value $\alpha_k = (f, e_k)$, and the minimum value of the left side is given by the first two terms on the right side. Since the left side cannot be negative, we obtain the important inequality

$$\sum_{k=1}^{n} |\alpha_k|^2 \leqslant \|f\|^2. \tag{2-26}$$

Since the right side of (2-26) is independent of n, we may, in case an *infinite* orthonormal set $e_1, e_2, \ldots$ exists, let n increase without bound on the left, and we thus conclude that the series $\sum_{k=1}^{\infty} |\alpha_k|^2$ converges, and that the sum does not exceed $\|f\|^2$. Both (2-26) and this strengthened form of (2-26) are known as "Bessel's inequality."

Now let $\mathscr{H}$ contain the countable orthonormal set $e_1, e_2, \ldots$; it is not required that these vectors should form a basis. For any vector f in $\mathscr{H}$ we form the inner products (f, e_k), $k = 1, 2, \ldots$ and we consider the sequence of vectors $f_1, f_2, \ldots$, where

$$f_n = \sum_{k=1}^{n} (f, e_k)e_k. \tag{2-27}$$

By a simple computation we find that, for $m < n$,

$$\|f_m - f_n\|^2 = \sum_{k=m+1}^{n} |(f, e_k)|^2. \tag{2-28}$$

Since, by Bessel's inequality, the series $\sum_{k=1}^{\infty} |(f, e_k)|^2$ converges, we can, for each positive number ϵ, find an integer N such that $\sum_{k=m+1}^{n} |(f, e_k)|^2 < \epsilon^2$, or $\|f_m - f_n\| < \epsilon$, whenever $N < m < n$. The sequence $f_1, f_2, \ldots$ therefore satisfies the Cauchy criterion, and since $\mathscr{H}$ is complete, there exists a vector g such that $\|g - f_n\| \to 0$. Furthermore, the vector $g - f$ is orthogonal to each of the vectors e_k. To see this, we observe that for $n > k$, $(g - f, e_k) = (g - f_n, e_k) + (f_n, e_k) - (f, e_k) = (g - f_n, e_k)$, since

$$(f_n, e_k) = \sum_{j=1}^{n} (f, e_j)(e_j, e_k) = (f, e_k).$$

Thus,

$$|(g - f, e_k)| = |(g - f_n, e_k)| \leqslant \|g - f_n\| \cdot \|e_k\| = \|g - f_n\| \to 0.$$

If the vectors $e_1, e_2, \ldots$ form a basis, we can prove that the vectors f and g are the same. We do this in the following way: Let $h = f - g$

and let any positive number ϵ be given. Since the vectors $e_1, e_2, \ldots$ form a basis, it is possible to find a *finite* linear combination, say $\gamma_1 e_1 + \gamma_2 e_2 + \cdots + \gamma_n e_n$, such that

$$\|h - (\gamma_1 e_1 + \gamma_2 e_2 + \cdots + \gamma_n e_n)\|^2 < \epsilon^2. \tag{2-29}$$

According to the argument presented at the beginning of this section, the left side of (2-29) is minimized by selecting each of the quantities γ_k equal to (h, e_k), or 0. Therefore, $\|h\| < \epsilon$, and from the arbitrariness of ϵ we conclude that $h = \theta$, or $f = g$.

If, on the other hand, the vectors $e_1, e_2, \ldots$ do *not* form a basis, then there exists a vector f that *cannot* be approximated arbitrarily closely by a combination of the e_k's. In this case it is evident that the vector $h = f - g$ (where g is, as above, the limit of the sequence of vectors f_n defined by (2-27)) is a nonzero vector.

By a slight modification of the above reasoning, we can easily prove the following: Given any infinite orthonormal set $e_1, e_2, \ldots$ in $\mathscr{H}$ and any sequence of complex numbers $\alpha_1, \alpha_2, \ldots$ such that the series $\sum_{k=1}^{\infty} |\alpha_k|^2$ converges, the sequence of vectors $f_1, f_2, \ldots$, where

$$f_n = \sum_{k=1}^{n} \alpha_k e_k, \tag{2-30}$$

converges to a vector f such that $(f, e_k) = \alpha_k$ for each k. Also,

$$\|f\|^2 = \sum_{k=1}^{\infty} |\alpha_k|^2. \tag{2-31}$$

Combining this assertion with the previous considerations of this section, we can easily prove that an orthonormal set $\{e_1, e_2, \ldots\}$ forms a basis of $\mathscr{H}$ if and only if the equality

$$\|f\|^2 = \sum_{k=1}^{\infty} |(f, e_k)|^2 \tag{2-32}$$

holds for every vector f. A simple extension of this result then shows that for any two vectors f and g, the inner product is given by the formula

$$(f, g) = \sum_{k=1}^{\infty} (f, e_k)\overline{(g, e_k)}. \tag{2-33}$$

This equality and the preceding one are both known as "Parseval's relation."

PROBLEMS

2-12. Prove (2-25) and show that, among all linear combinations of the vectors $e_1, e_2, \ldots, e_n$, the particular combination $\alpha_1 e_1 + \alpha_2 e_2 + \cdots + \alpha_n e_n$ may be characterized as follows: The vector $f - \sum_{k=1}^{n} \beta_k e_k$ is orthogonal to each of the vectors e_k if and only if $\beta_k = \alpha_k$, $k = 1, 2, \ldots, n$.

2-13. Suppose that $\mathscr{H}$ possesses an uncountable orthonormal set S of vectors. Prove that a vector f is orthogonal to all except a finite or countable subset of the vectors in S.

2-14. Prove the statements contained in the last two paragraphs of Section 2-4.

¶ **2-5** A subset S of a linear space is said to be "convex" if for every pair of vectors f and g contained in S and for every real number t satisfying the inequalities $0 \leqslant t \leqslant 1$ the vector $tf + (1 - t)g$ is also contained in S. Convex sets possess a remarkable property, which is expressed in the following theorem:

Every (nonempty) closed convex subset S of a Hilbert space contains a vector whose norm is less than that of any other vector contained in S.

The proof proceeds as follows: If δ denotes the greatest lower bound of norms of vectors contained in S, then there exists a sequence $f_1, f_2, \ldots$ of vectors whose norms converge to δ. Given any positive number ϵ, we can determine an integer N such that $\|f_n\|^2 < \delta^2 + \epsilon$ whenever n exceeds N. From the identity

$$\|\tfrac{1}{2}(f_n - f_m)\|^2 = \tfrac{1}{2}\|f_n\|^2 + \tfrac{1}{2}\|f_m\|^2 - \|\tfrac{1}{2}(f_n + f_m)\|^2, \quad (2\text{-}34)$$

and the fact that $\tfrac{1}{2}(f_n + f_m)$ is contained in S (corresponding to the choice $t = \tfrac{1}{2}$ in the above definition of convexity), we find that

$$\|\tfrac{1}{2}(f_n - f_m)\|^2 < \tfrac{1}{2}(\delta^2 + \epsilon) + \tfrac{1}{2}(\delta^2 + \epsilon) - \delta^2 = \epsilon \quad (2\text{-}35)$$

or

$$\|f_m - f_n\| < 2\epsilon^{1/2} \quad (2\text{-}36)$$

whenever m and n exceed N. The inequality (2-36) asserts that the sequence under consideration is a Cauchy sequence, and by completeness it follows that there exists a vector f that is the limit of this sequence. Furthermore, since S is assumed closed, f must be contained in S. Finally, by writing the triangle inequality in the form

$$\|f\| \leqslant \|f - f_n\| + \|f_n\| \quad (2\text{-}37)$$

and taking account of the limit conditions $\|f - f_n\| \to 0$, $\|f_n\| \to \delta$, we conclude that $\|f\| \leqslant \delta$; on the other hand, since f is contained in S, $\|f\| \geqslant \delta$. Hence, $\|f\| = \delta$, so it has been shown that S contains a vector whose norm is *at least as small* as that of any other vector contained in S. Now suppose that there were a vector g in S distinct from f and also having norm δ. Then from the equality [cf. (2-34)]

$$\|\tfrac{1}{2}(f + g)\|^2 = \tfrac{1}{2}\|f\|^2 + \tfrac{1}{2}\|g\|^2 - \|\tfrac{1}{2}(f - g)\|^2, \qquad (2\text{-}38)$$

we observe that the right side is definitely less than δ^2, and so the vector $\tfrac{1}{2}(f + g)$ would, on the one hand, have a norm smaller than δ, and would, on the other hand, be contained in S (again on account of the convexity of S). This would contradict the definition of δ, and so the theorem is proven.

Of particular importance in later applications will be the following example of a closed convex subset in $\mathscr{L}_2(D)$: Consider the set S of all functions that are contained in $\mathscr{L}_2(D)$ and have the value λ at an arbitrary but fixed point t of D. Then S is evidently a nonempty * convex set; to show that it is closed, we consider any function f that is a limit point of S. Then we can select a sequence $f_1, f_2, \ldots$ of functions belonging to S such that $\|f - f_n\|$ approaches 0 with increasing n. According to the inequality (1-4),

$$|f(t) - \lambda| = |f(t) - f_n(t)| \leqslant c(t)\,\|f - f_n\|. \qquad (2\text{-}39)$$

Since the right side of (2-39) approaches 0, the left side must vanish, showing that f, like each member of the sequence, assumes the value λ at t. Therefore, f is contained in S; therefore, S is closed. Choosing, in particular, λ equal to unity, we have proven that, given any point t of D, there exists a unique solution to the problem of minimizing $\|f\|$ among all functions in $\mathscr{L}_2(D)$ that satisfy the condition $f(t) = 1$. This problem will be considered in some detail in Chapter 3.

PROBLEM

2-15. Prove that the set of all polynomials of degree not exceeding k, k being a fixed positive integer, is a closed convex subset of $\mathscr{L}_2(D)$. *Hint:* Use the Cauchy integral formula to show that the uniform limit of polynomials of *bounded* degree is itself a polynomial.

---

* The function $f \equiv \lambda$ belongs to $\mathscr{L}_2(D)$, since D is assumed bounded, and hence of finite area. (Cf. footnote, p. 1.)

¶ **2-6**   Our purpose in this section is to prove the "projection theorem," which may be stated as follows:

Given a closed linear manifold S in a Hilbert space $\mathscr{H}$, every vector f in $\mathscr{H}$ is expressible, in a unique manner, in the form

$$f = g + h, \quad g \in S, \quad h \in S^{\perp}. \tag{2-40}$$

The uniqueness of this representation is proved quite simply, for if a second representation, $f = \tilde{g} + \tilde{h}$, were possible, we would obtain the equality $g + h = \tilde{g} + \tilde{h}$, or $g - \tilde{g} = \tilde{h} - h$. On the one hand, $g - \tilde{g}$ is contained in S, whereas $\tilde{h} - h$ is contained in $S^{\perp}$ (since both S and $S^{\perp}$ are linear manifolds). Therefore, $g - \tilde{g}$ must be contained both in S and $S^{\perp}$, and so $(g - \tilde{g}, g - \tilde{g}) = 0$, or $g - \tilde{g} = \theta$. Therefore, $g = \tilde{g}$ and $h = \tilde{h}$. The *existence* of the representation (2-40) is demonstrated as follows. Let $\tilde{S}$ denote the set of all vectors expressible in the form $f - e$, where $e \in S$. It is evident that, like S, $\tilde{S}$ is both closed and convex. By the principal result of Section 2-5, there exists an element g in S such that the inequality $\|f - g\| \leqslant \|f - \tilde{g}\|$ holds for every vector $\tilde{g}$ in S. If g_1 denotes any vector in S and ϵ denotes any real number, then we may replace $\tilde{g}$ in the above inequality by $g + \epsilon g_1$, and so we obtain the inequality $\|f - g\|^2 \leqslant \|(f - g) - \epsilon g_1\|^2$, which can be rewritten in the equivalent form (cf. Problem 2-16),

$$2\epsilon \operatorname{Re}(f - g, g_1) - \epsilon^2 \|g_1\|^2 \leqslant 0. \tag{2-41}$$

Unless $\operatorname{Re}(f - g, g_1)$ vanished, the left side of (2-41) would change sign as ϵ changes sign, so that (2-41) would be violated for a suitable choice of ϵ. Therefore, $\operatorname{Re}(f - g, g_1)$ must vanish. Replacing g_1 in this argument by ig_1 (or by restricting ϵ to purely imaginary values instead of real values), we find that $\operatorname{Im}(f - g, g_1) = 0$. Therefore, $(f - g, g_1) = 0$, and so the vector $f - g$ is contained in $S^{\perp}$. The representation (2-40) is thus accomplished (with $h = f - g$).

The vector g associated with f in (2-40) is termed the "orthogonal projection" of f upon the closed linear manifold S.

PROBLEM

2-16.   Work out the details leading to (2-41).

¶ **2-7** By a "functional" we mean a function that associates with each vector f of a linear space a complex number $l(f)$. A simple example of a functional in the space $\mathscr{L}_2(D)$, and an especially important one for our purposes, is the one that associates with each function $f(z)$ belonging to $\mathscr{L}_2(D)$ the number $f(t)$, where t denotes a specified point of D. A functional is said to be linear if for every pair of vectors f, g and every pair of complex numbers α, β the equality $l(\alpha f + \beta g) = \alpha l(f) + \beta l(g)$ is satisfied. Finally, a functional defined on an inner-product space is said to be "bounded" if there exists a positive number C such that the inequality $|l(f)| \leqslant C\|f\|$ holds for every vector f. Taking account of (1-4) we observe that the functional defined above is bounded, and it is evidently also linear.

If e denotes a fixed vector of the Hilbert space $\mathscr{H}$, the functional

$$l(f) = (f, e) \tag{2-42}$$

is obviously linear, whereas from the Schwarz inequality we obtain $|l(f)| \leqslant C\|f\|$, where $C = \|e\|$, so that l is bounded. Now we prove a remarkable converse to this observation.

With each bounded linear functional l there is associated a unique vector e such that (2-42) holds for all vectors f.

The *uniqueness* is easily settled by the observation that if $(f, e) = (f, e')$ holds for all vectors f, it holds in particular for $f = e - e'$, and so $(e - e', e) = (e - e', e')$, or $(e - e', e - e') = \|e - e'\|^2 = 0$, whence $e = e'$. The *existence* of the vector e is established by the following argument. If $l(f) = 0$ for all vectors f, then $e = \theta$ will obviously suffice; otherwise the set S consisting of all vectors f such that $l(f) = 0$ fails to exhaust $\mathscr{H}$. Since S is, on account of the boundedness of l, easily seen to be a *closed* linear manifold, it follows from the principal result of Section 2-6 that there exists a nonzero vector h that is orthogonal to S. [We simply choose some vector f that is not contained in S and then determine the corresponding vector h appearing in (2-40).] Expressing any vector f in the form

$$f = (f - ch) + ch, \quad c = l(f)/l(h), \tag{2-43}$$

we observe that $l(f - ch) = l(f) - cl(h) = 0$, so that $f - ch$ belongs to S. Hence, $(f - ch, h) = 0$, and so $(f, h) = c(h, h)$, or

$$l(f) = \frac{l(h)}{(h, h)} (f, h). \tag{2-44}$$

This may be written in the form

$$l(f) = \left(f, \frac{\overline{l(h)}}{(h, h)} h \right), \tag{2-45}$$

which coincides with (2-42) if e is identified with $\{\overline{l(h)}/(h, h)h\}$. The proof is thus complete. It may be noted, incidentally, that, aside from the trivial case $l(f) \equiv 0$, when $S = \mathscr{H}$, the orthogonal complement $S^\perp$ is one-dimensional, consisting precisely of all scalar multiples of any one of the nonzero vectors that it contains. Also, if the norm or bound of a bounded linear functional (denoted $\|l\|$) is defined as the least value of C for which the inequality $|l(f)| \leqslant C\|f\|$ always holds, it is readily seen, by choosing $f = e$, that $\|l\| = \|e\|$—i.e., the norm of a bounded linear functional is equal to the norm of the vector which is associated with the functional, in accordance with the above theorem.

PROBLEM

2-17. Prove that, in $\mathscr{L}_2(D)$, the functional $f'(t)$ is bounded, where t is a fixed point of the domain D.

3

The Reproducing Kernel of a Domain

¶ **3-1** According to (1-4), the functional that assigns to each function $f(z)$ belonging to $\mathscr{L}_2(D)$ its value at a specified point t of the domain D is bounded and linear. It then follows from the principal result of Section 2-7 that for each point t of D there exists a uniquely determined function in $\mathscr{L}_2(D)$, which we momentarily denote as $g_{(t)}(z)$, such that the following equality holds for every function $f(z)$ belonging to $\mathscr{L}_2(D)$:

$$f(t) = (f, g_{(t)}) = \int\int_D f(z)\overline{g_{(t)}(z)} \, dx \, dy. \tag{3-1}$$

Taking for $f(z)$ the function $g_{(\tau)}(z)$, τ being either t or any other point of D, we obtain $g_{(\tau)}(t) = (g_{(\tau)}, g_{(t)}) = \overline{(g_{(t)}, g_{(\tau)})} = \overline{g_{(t)}(\tau)}$. We have thus shown that $g_{(t)}(z)$, considered as a function of the two arguments z and t, is "hermitian-symmetric"—i.e., interchanging the arguments converts the functional value into its conjugate. In particular, it follows that $g_{(t)}(t)$ must be real. In fact, a stronger statement is true—namely, that $g_{(t)}(t)$ is positive—for $g_{(t)}(t) = (g_{(t)}, g_{(t)}) = \|g_{(t)}\|^2 > 0$. [If $\|g_t\|$ were to vanish, (3-1) would imply that *every* function belonging to $\mathscr{L}_2(D)$ must vanish at t, and this contradicts the fact that every constant function belongs to $\mathscr{L}_2(D)$.]

We now denote $g_{(t)}(z)$ by $K(z, t)$, so that the condition of hermitian symmetry assumes the form

$$K(z, t) = \overline{K(t, z)}. \tag{3-2}$$

The equation (3-1), which uniquely characterizes $K(z, t)$ within the space $\mathscr{L}_2(D)$, assumes the form

$$f(t) = \int\int_D f(z)\overline{K(z, t)} \, dx \, dy. \tag{3-3}$$

The function $K(z, t)$ is known as the "reproducing kernel" of the domain D; the justification of the terminology is apparent from (3-3).

¶ **3-2** The determination of the reproducing kernel of a disc is especially simple, because every function analytic in such a domain can be represented by a single power series. For convenience we take D to be the unit disc, $|z| < 1$, leaving the case of an arbitrary disc to Problem 3-2.

We begin with the following observations, whose proofs are left as Problem 3-1:

(a) A function $f(z)$ analytic in D belongs to $\mathscr{L}_2(D)$ if and only if the coefficients of its Taylor series,

$$f(z) = a_0 + a_1 z + a_2 z^2 + \cdots \tag{3-4}$$

satisfy the condition

$$\sum_{n=0}^{\infty} \frac{|a_n|^2}{n + 1} < \infty. \tag{3-5}$$

(b) If $f(z)$ and $g(z)$, both belonging to $\mathscr{L}_2(D)$, possess the expansions (3-4) and

$$g(z) = b_0 + b_1 z + b_2 z^2 + \cdots, \tag{3-6}$$

respectively, then

$$(f, g) = \pi \sum_{n=0}^{\infty} \frac{a_n \overline{b_n}}{n + 1}. \tag{3-7}$$

[In particular, (f, f) is given, aside from a factor of π, by the left side of (3-5).]

Now, choosing for $g(z)$ the kernel $K(z, t)$ (so that the coefficients b_n depend on t), and taking $f(z)$ as z^n, $n = 0, 1, 2, \ldots$, we obtain from (3-3) and (3-7) the result

$$t^n = \frac{\pi \bar{b}_n}{n + 1}. \tag{3-8}$$

Thus, $b_n = (n + 1)\bar{t}^n/\pi$, and so

$$\pi K(z, t) = \sum_{n=0}^{\infty} (n + 1)(z\bar{t})^n. \tag{3-9}$$

Now, differentiation of the expansion

$$\frac{1}{1 - w} = \sum_{n=0}^{\infty} w^n \qquad (|w| < 1) \tag{3-10}$$

furnishes the expansion

$$\frac{1}{(1 - w)^2} = \sum_{n=0}^{\infty} n w^{n-1} = \sum_{n=0}^{\infty} (n + 1) w^n. \tag{3-11}$$

Identifying w in (3-11) with $z\bar{t}$ in (3-9), we conclude that

$$K(z, t) = \frac{1}{\pi (1 - z\bar{t})^2}. \tag{3-12}$$

Later we shall derive the formula (3-12) in several other ways.

PROBLEMS

3-1. Prove the assertions (a) and (b) made on p. 22. *Hint:* Begin by proving that (when D is the unit disc)

$$(z^n, z^m) = \begin{cases} 0 & \text{if } n \neq m, \\ \dfrac{\pi}{n + 1} & \text{if } n = m. \end{cases}$$

3-2. Determine the reproducing kernel of the disc $|z - z_0| < R$.

¶ **3-3** In Section 2-5 it was shown that the problem of minimizing $\|f\|$ among all functions that belong to $\mathscr{L}_2(D)$ and satisfy the condition $f(t) = 1$ possesses a unique solution. We can now express the solution in terms of the kernel $K(z, t)$. For any "competing" function $f(z)$ we obtain, by employing the Schwarz inequality and the reproducing property of $K(z, t)$:

$$1 = |f(t)|^2 = |(f, K(z, t))|^2 \leqslant (f, f)(K(z, t), K(z, t)) = \|f\|^2 K(t, t). \tag{3-13}$$

Therefore, $\|f\|^2 \geqslant 1/K(t, t)$, and (as we see by recalling the derivation of the Schwarz inequality) equality holds if and only if $f(z)$ is a constant multiple of $K(z, t)$. The condition $f(t) = 1$ furnishes for the constant factor the value $1/K(t, t)$. Thus, we have obtained the striking result that the minimum value of $\|f\|^2$, subject to the condition $f(t) = 1$, is equal to $1/K(t, t)$, and that the only function for which the minimum value is attained is $K(z, t)/K(t, t)$.

More generally, let a finite number of distinct points $t_1, t_2, \ldots, t_n$ be selected in D and let us seek to minimize $\|f\|$ among all functions $f(z)$ belonging to $\mathscr{L}_2(D)$ and satisfying the conditions $f(t_k) = \alpha_k$ ($k = 1, 2, \ldots, n$), where the α_k are prescribed constants. The existence and uniqueness of a solution to this problem is established by an obvious generalization of the argument presented in Section 2-5 for the case $n = 1$. In order to obtain an explicit expression for the minimizing function, we reason as follows: Let S denote the set of all functions expressible as linear combinations of $K(z, t_1)$, $K(z, t_2)$, $\ldots$, and $K(z, t_n)$. Clearly, S is a finite–dimensional inner-product space, and it is therefore, by Problem 2-9, complete. If we now consider S as a subset of $\mathscr{L}_2(D)$, it is therefore a closed linear manifold of $\mathscr{L}_2(D)$. We express the extremal function $f(z)$, in accordance with the projection theorem, as $g(z) + h(z)$, where $g(z) \in S$ and $h(z) \in S^{\perp}$. Then we observe that [since $h(t_j) = (h, K(z, t_j)) = 0$ for $j = 1, 2, \ldots, n$] $g(t_j) = f(t_j) = \alpha_j$, so that $g(z)$ is also a "competing" function. Furthermore, since $\|f\|^2 = \|g\|^2 + \|h\|^2$, it follows that $h(z) \equiv 0$, for otherwise $g(z)$ would have a smaller norm than $f(z)$, in contradiction with the minimal property of $f(z)$. Thus, $f(z)$ must admit a representation

$$f(z) = \sum_{j=1}^{n} c_j K(z, t_j). \tag{3-14}$$

The coefficients c_j are obtained by assigning to z and $f(z)$ in turn the values $t_1, t_2, \ldots, t_n$ and $\alpha_1, \alpha_2, \ldots, \alpha_n$, respectively. In this manner we are led to the system of linear algebraic equations

$$\alpha_k = \sum_{j=1}^{n} c_j K(t_k, t_j) \qquad (k = 1, 2, \ldots, n). \tag{3-15}$$

It is to be emphasized that the determinant of this system, namely

$$\begin{vmatrix} K(t_1, t_1) & K(t_1, t_2) & \cdots & K(t_1, t_n) \\ K(t_2, t_1) & K(t_2, t_2) & \cdots & K(t_2, t_n) \\ \vdots & \vdots & & \vdots \\ K(t_n, t_1) & K(t_n, t_2) & \cdots & K(t_n, t_n) \end{vmatrix},$$

cannot vanish, for if it did vanish we would be able to make a specific choice of the numbers $\alpha_1, \alpha_2, \ldots, \alpha_n$ for which the system (3-15) would be unsolvable, and this would contradict the fact that the extremal problem under consideration is solvable for *every* choice of these numbers. Once the system (3-15) has been solved, the minimizing function $f(z)$ is known, and we get for the square of the minimum norm the expression

$$\|f\|^2 = \sum_{j,k=1}^{n} c_j \bar{c}_k (K(z, t_j), K(z, t_k))$$

$$= \sum_{j,k=1}^{n} c_j \bar{c}_k K(t_k, t_j). \tag{3-16}$$

Taking account of (3-15) we get the more concise expression

$$\|f\|^2 = \sum_{k=1}^{n} \bar{c}_k \alpha_k. \tag{3-17}$$

If we first prescribe arbitrarily the c's and then compute the α's from the system (3-15), we see, from the nonvanishing of the determinant of the system, that all the α's will vanish only if all the c's vanish. It follows that the expression $\sum_{j,k=1}^{n} c_j \bar{c}_k K(t_k, t_j)$ appearing in (3-16) assumes a positive value for every choice of the c's except the trivial one—namely $c_1 = c_2 = \cdots = c_n = 0$. Using the terminology of linear algebra, we have thus shown that the hermitian form $\sum_{j,k=1}^{n} c_j \bar{c}_k K(t_k, t_j)$ is positive definite. One of the basic theorems of linear algebra asserts that the determinant of the matrix of coefficients of a positive definite form is positive. Therefore, the determinant of the system (3-15) is positive (not merely nonzero, as shown previously). That the determinant possesses a *real* value follows immediately from the hermitian symmetry of the entries: $K(t_j, t_k) = \overline{K(t_k, t_j)}$.

PROBLEMS

3-3. Setting $t = 0$ in (3-12) and taking account of the minimal property of the kernel, we find that the minimum of (f, f) under the conditions $f(z) \in \mathscr{L}_2(D)$, $f(0) = 1$ is equal to π. Deduce this result directly from the reasoning employed in Chapter 1.

3-4. Confirm the assertion made in the text, concerning the positive character of the determinant which follows (3-15), in the particular case of the unit disc. for two points. Use the explicit formula for the kernel.

3-5. Observe that when t is set equal to 0 in (3-12), the kernel reduces to the constant $1/\pi$. Prove that if, for some domain D and some point t of D, the kernel reduces (as a function of z) to a constant, this constant must equal the reciprocal of the area of D.

¶ **3-4**   We now prove the assertion made in Section 2-3 that $\mathscr{L}_2(D)$ is separable. Let us choose any denumerable set S of points which is dense in D, and let us enumerate them: $t_1, t_2, \ldots$. (For example, we may choose the set of all points in D whose real and imaginary parts are both rational.) Now, a function in $\mathscr{L}_2(D)$ that is orthogonal to each of the functions $K(z, t_k)$ must vanish at all points of S, and it then follows by continuity that this function must vanish identically. It follows from the reasoning employed in Section 2-3 that when the Gram–Schmidt process is carried out on the sequence $\{K(z, t_k)\}$, an orthonormal basis of $\mathscr{L}_2(D)$ is obtained. Since $\mathscr{L}_2(D)$ possesses a countable orthonormal basis, it is separable.

We note that every finite subset of the set of functions $K(z, t_k)$ is linearly independent. For, suppose that there existed indices $j_1, j_2, \ldots, j_n$ and nonzero coefficients $c_1, c_2, \ldots, c_n$ such that $\sum_{k=1}^{n} c_k K(z, t_{j_k}) \equiv 0$. It would then follow from the reproducing property (3-3) of the kernel that $c_1 f(t_{j_1}) + c_2 f(t_{j_2}) + \cdots + c_n f(t_{j_n})$ must vanish for *every* function $f(z)$ belonging to $\mathscr{L}_2(D)$. However, if we choose for $f(z)$ the polynomial

$$\prod_{k=2}^{n} (z - t_{j_k}),$$

which vanishes at $t_{j_2}, t_{j_3}, \ldots, t_{j_n}$ but not at t_{j_1}, we would obtain the result $c_1 = 0$. It therefore follows that the Gram–Schmidt process can be applied directly to the sequence $\{K(z, t_k)\}$, without first suppressing any members of the sequence.

We also remark that instead of choosing a set of points $\{t_k\}$ that is dense in D, it would suffice to select a set of points, say $\{\tau_k\}$, possessing at least one limit point in D; a function $f(z)$ in $\mathscr{L}_2(D)$ that is orthogonal to each of the functions $\{K(z, \tau_k)\}$ must vanish at each τ_k, and this suffices, on account of the analyticity of each member of $\mathscr{L}_2(D)$, to assure the identical vanishing of $f(z)$. Therefore, applying the Gram–Schmidt procedure to the sequence of functions $\{K(z, \tau_k)\}$ again furnishes a denumerable orthonormal basis of $\mathscr{L}_2(D)$.

PROBLEM

3-6. Let t be any point of D, and let any positive number ϵ be given. Prove that there exists a finite set of points $t_1, t_2, \ldots, t_n$, each different from t, and a set of numbers $\{c_1, c_2, \ldots, c_n\}$ such that

$$\left\| K(z, t) - \sum_{k=1}^{n} c_k K(z, t_k) \right\| < \epsilon.$$

¶ **3-5** Having established the separability of $\mathscr{L}_2(D)$, we now proceed to obtain a striking expansion formula for the kernel $K(z, t)$. Let $\{\phi_1(z), \phi_2(z), \ldots\}$ be any orthonormal basis of $\mathscr{L}_2(D)$. Then we know that every function $f(z)$ belonging to $\mathscr{L}_2(D)$ can be expressed in the form

$$f(z) = \sum_{k=1}^{\infty} (f, \phi_k)\phi_k(z). \tag{3-18}$$

This series converges pointwise—in fact, uniformly on compact subsets of D—and also in the sense that

$$\lim_{n \to \infty} \left\| f - \sum_{k=1}^{n} (f, \phi_k)\phi_k \right\| = 0. \tag{3-19}$$

If we choose for $f(z)$ the function $K(z, t)$, where t is any point of D, the coefficients (f, ϕ_k) appearing in (3-18) assume the form

$$(K(z, t), \phi_k) = \overline{(\phi_k, K(z, t))}.$$

Taking account of the reproducing property (3-3) of the kernel, we obtain, as a particular case of (3-18), the bilinear expansion

$$K(z, t) = \sum_{k=1}^{\infty} \overline{\phi_k(t)}\phi_k(z). \tag{3-20}$$

Once a set of functions dense in $\mathscr{L}_2(D)$ is known, the Gram–Schmidt procedure may be used to construct an orthonormal basis $\{\phi_1, \phi_2, \ldots\}$, and hence the kernel $K(z, t)$. In fact, it evidently suffices to begin with a set of functions, say $\{\psi_1, \psi_2, \ldots\}$, whose linear combinations are dense in $\mathscr{L}_2(D)$ (or, what comes to the same thing, no function of positive norm shall be orthogonal to each function of the set *). We remark, without going into the proof, that, if D is simply connected and bounded by a Jordan curve, the polynomials are

---

* A set of elements in a Hilbert space $\mathscr{H}$ possessing this property is said to "span" $\mathscr{H}$.

dense in $\mathscr{L}_2(D)$. Therefore, by applying the Gram–Schmidt process to the sequence of functions $\{1, z, z^2, \ldots\}$ we obtain a set of *polynomials* that constitute an orthonormal basis. Thus, the construction of the kernel is reduced to a denumerable sequence of integrations over D and elementary algebraic operations. A similar procedure may be employed for multiply connected domains whose boundary components satisfy appropriate conditions.

PROBLEMS

3-7. Carry out the Gram–Schmidt procedure on the functions $1, z, z^2, \ldots$ in the unit disc, and compute the kernel with the aid of (3-20).

3-8. Prove that the polynomials are *not* dense in $\mathscr{L}_2(D)$ when D consists of the unit disc minus a radial segment.

¶ **3-6**   Although the bilinear expansion (3-20) of the kernel $K(z, t)$ holds for *every* choice of an orthonormal basis in $\mathscr{L}_2(D)$, a *particular* basis may prove to be especially useful in the study of a certain class of problems. In this section we show how to construct a basis that is especially useful in the solution of extremal problems of a type to be described in detail in the following section.

We begin by introducing the following notation: Let t denote a specified point of the domain D, and let constants $\alpha_0, \alpha_1, \alpha_2, \ldots, \alpha_n$ be given. Then by $f^{\alpha_0 \alpha_1 \cdots \alpha_n}(z)$ we mean the function belonging to $\mathscr{L}_2(D)$, satisfying the conditions $f(t) = \alpha_0, f'(t) = \alpha_1, \ldots, f^{(n)}(t) = \alpha_n$, and having the smallest possible norm, whereas $\lambda^{\alpha_0 \alpha_1 \cdots \alpha_n}$ denotes the quantity $\|f^{\alpha_0 \alpha_1 \cdots \alpha_n}\|^2$; the existence and uniqueness of $f^{\alpha_0 \alpha_1 \cdots \alpha_n}$ is established by an obvious extension of the reasoning used in the preceding chapter. The quantity $\lambda^{\alpha_0 \alpha_1 \cdots \alpha_n}$ is, from its very definition, positive except in the trivial case $\alpha_0 = \alpha_1 = \cdots = \alpha_n = 0$. In particular, the first result of Section 3-3 can be summed up in the following form: $f^1(z) = K(z, t)/K(t, t)$, $\lambda^1 = 1/K(t, t)$.

It should be stressed that the extremal function $f^{\alpha_0 \alpha_1 \cdots \alpha_n}(z)$ and the number $\lambda^{\alpha_0 \alpha_1 \cdots \alpha_n}$ depend on the point t as well as on the prescribed numbers $\alpha_0, \alpha_1, \ldots, \alpha_n$; however, notational reference to t is usually omitted.

Now consider the sequence of functions

$$\frac{f^1(z)}{\sqrt{\lambda^1}}, \frac{f^{01}(z)}{\sqrt{\lambda^{01}}}, \frac{f^{001}(z)}{\sqrt{\lambda^{001}}}, \ldots.$$

The norm of each one of these functions is evidently equal to unity. To show that these functions constitute an orthogonal set, we begin by showing that a function $g(z)$ belonging to $\mathscr{L}_2(D)$ is orthogonal to $f^1(z)$ if and only if $g(t)$ vanishes. For, on the one hand, if $g(t) = 0$, then, by the very definition of $f^1(z)$, $\|f^1(z) + \epsilon g(z)\|^2 \geqslant \|f^1(z)\|^2$ for every number ϵ. Choosing ϵ real, we obtain $\epsilon(2\,\mathrm{Re}\,(f^1, g) + \epsilon\|g\|^2) \geqslant 0$, and so, as in the proof of the projection theorem, $\mathrm{Re}\,(f^1, g) = 0$; similarly, $\mathrm{Im}\,(f^1, g) = 0$, and so $(f^1, g) = 0$. Conversely, if $(f^1, g) = 0$, we have the equality $\|f^1 + \epsilon g\|^2 = \|f^1\|^2 + |\epsilon|^2\|g\|^2 = \lambda^1 + |\epsilon|^2\|g\|^2$, whereas, from the fact that $(f^1(z) + \epsilon g(z))/(1 + \epsilon g(t))$ is a "competing" function, we obtain the *inequality*

$$\|f^1 + \epsilon g\|^2 \geqslant \lambda^1|1 + \epsilon g(t)|^2,$$

which can be rewritten as

$$\lambda^1 + |\epsilon|^2\|g\|^2 \geqslant \lambda^1|1 + \epsilon g(t)|^2;$$

this reduces, for real values of ϵ, to

$$\epsilon[2\lambda^1\,\mathrm{Re}\,g(t) + \epsilon(\lambda^1|g(t)|^2 - \|g\|^2)] \geqslant 0.$$

Again arguing as in the proof of the projection theorem, we conclude that $\lambda^1\,\mathrm{Re}\,g(t) = 0$; hence, $\mathrm{Re}\,g(t)$, and similarly $\mathrm{Im}\,g(t)$, must vanish. Thus, $g(t)$ must vanish, as was to be proven.

Likewise, one can show that a function $g(z)$ belonging to $\mathscr{L}_2(D)$ is orthogonal to the first n functions of the sequence

$$\{f^1(z), f^{01}(z), \ldots\}$$

if and only if $g(t) = g'(t) = \cdots = g^{(n-1)}(t) = 0$. In particular, each function of this sequence is orthogonal to each of its "predecessors" and (by symmetry) to each of its "successors." Thus, as asserted above, this sequence constitutes an orthogonal set of functions. A function belonging to $\mathscr{L}_2(D)$ that is orthogonal to each member of this sequence must, by the foregoing argument, vanish at t, together with each of its derivatives. By one of the basic results of the theory of analytic functions, such a function must vanish identically in D. By the reasoning employed in the preceding section, it now follows that the functions $\{f^1/\sqrt{\lambda^1}, f^{01}/\sqrt{\lambda^{01}}, \ldots\}$ constitute an orthonormal basis in $\mathscr{L}_2(D)$. With this choice of a basis the expansion (3-20) assumes the form

$$K(z, \tau) = \frac{f^1(z)\overline{f^1(\tau)}}{\lambda^1} + \frac{f^{01}(z)\overline{f^{01}(\tau)}}{\lambda^{01}} + \cdots. \qquad (3\text{-}21)$$

[Note that (3-21) is valid for all points τ in D, not merely for $\tau = t$].

¶ **3-7**　The basis of $\mathscr{L}_2(D)$ developed in Section 3-6 enables us to solve a certain class of extremal problems by elementary algebraic methods. For the sake of definiteness, let us begin with the problem of determining $f^{\alpha_0\alpha_1}$ and $\lambda^{\alpha_0\alpha_1}$. (It is evident that $f^{\alpha_0} = \alpha_0 f^1$ and $\lambda^{\alpha_0} = |\alpha_0|^2\lambda^1$.) We know that an expansion of the form

$$f^{\alpha_0\alpha_1}(z) = c_0 f^1(z) + c_1 f^{01}(z) + \cdots \tag{3-22}$$

must hold, both in the sense of convergence in norm and in the sense of regular convergence, since the functions $f^1(z), f^{01}(z), \ldots$ constitute an orthogonal basis in $\mathscr{L}_2(D)$. Now, it is evident that the remainder of the series appearing in (3-22), indicated by $\ldots$, vanishes, together with its first derivative, at t, and that the remainder is orthogonal to the expression that is explicitly written out. Thus, the remainder, unless it vanished identically, would increase the norm of the right side of (3-22) without affecting the values at t of the sum of the series and of its derivative. Taking account of the minimizing property of $f^{\alpha_0\alpha_1}$, we conclude that the latter can be expressed as a finite sum:

$$f^{\alpha_0\alpha_1}(z) = c_0 f^1(z) + c_1 f^{01}(z). \tag{3-23}$$

Setting $z = t$ and taking account of the vanishing of $f^{01}(t)$, we immediately obtain $c_0 = \alpha_0$. Similarly, differentiating both sides of (3-23) and setting $z = t$, we obtain (recalling that $f^{01\prime}(t) = 1$): $\alpha_1 = c_0 f^{1\prime}(t) + c_1$, or $c_1 = \alpha_1 - c_0 f^{1\prime}(t) = \alpha_1 - \alpha_0 f^{1\prime}(t)$. Hence, $f^{\alpha_0\alpha_1}$ is completely determined, and is given explicitly by the equation

$$f^{\alpha_0\alpha_1}(z) = \alpha_0 f^1(z) + (\alpha_1 - \alpha_0 f^{1\prime}(t)) f^{01}(z). \tag{3-24}$$

Furthermore, by taking the inner product of each side of (3-24) with itself, exploiting the orthogonality of f^1 and f^{01}, and recalling the definitions of the λ's, we obtain:

$$\lambda^{\alpha_0\alpha_1} = |\alpha_0|^2\lambda^1 + |\alpha_1 - \alpha_0 f^{1\prime}(t)|^2\lambda^{01}. \tag{3-25}$$

This procedure obviously extends to the determination of $f^{\alpha_0\alpha_1\cdots\alpha_n}$ and $\lambda^{\alpha_0\alpha_1\cdots\alpha_n}$. On the other hand, a slight complication arises when one or more of the conditions preceding the final one—namely, $f^{(n)}(t) = \alpha_n$—are omitted, for, although it is evident that the extremal function exists and must consist of a linear combination of the functions $f^1, f^{01}, \ldots, f^{00\cdots01}$ (as is the case with $f^{\alpha_0\alpha_1\cdots\alpha_n}$), the $n + 1$ coefficients are no longer unambiguously determined by the prescribed α's, which now number fewer than $n + 1$. To take the simplest possible problem of this type, let us seek to minimize $\|f\|$, subject to the single restriction $f'(t) = 1$; note that no restriction is placed on the value of $f(t)$. We denote the (unique) extremal function as f^{*1}, and the square of its norm as λ^{*1}. (The appropriate notation for more complicated problems of this type is obvious; the omission of a condition is always indicated by an asterisk.) In complete analogy with (3-23), we see that $f^{*1}(z)$ is expressible in the form

$$f^{*1}(z) = d_0 f^1(z) + d_1 f^{01}(z). \tag{3-26}$$

In contrast to (3-23), only one relationship between d_0 and d_1 is determined by the prescribed data, namely

$$1 = d_0 f^{1\prime}(t) + d_1. \tag{3-27}$$

However, we may now deduce from (3-26) the equality

$$\lambda^{*1} = |d_0|^2 \lambda^1 + |d_1|^2 \lambda^{01}. \tag{3-28}$$

Thus, we find that the problem of determining f^{*1} and λ^{*1} is equivalent to that of choosing the complex numbers d_0 and d_1, subject to the restriction (3-27), so as to minimize the right-hand side of (3-28). Although such a problem can easily be solved by the method of Lagrange multipliers, it is easier and more instructive to treat the problem by purely elementary algebraic methods. If we momentarily perform the substitutions $e_0 = d_0 \sqrt{\lambda^1}$ and $e_1 = d_1 \sqrt{\lambda^{01}}$, we may restate our problem in the form: To minimize $|e_1|^2 + |e_2|^2$ subject to the constraint

$$1 = e_0 \frac{f^{1\prime}(t)}{\sqrt{\lambda^1}} + e_1 \frac{1}{\sqrt{\lambda^{01}}}. \tag{3-29}$$

Let us consider two-dimensional unitary space—i.e., the set of all ordered pairs of complex numbers $\{\alpha_1, \alpha_2\}$, with inner product defined as follows:

$$(\{\alpha_1, \alpha_2\}, \{\beta_1, \beta_2\}) = \alpha_1 \bar{\beta}_1 + \alpha_2 \bar{\beta}_2. \tag{3-30}$$

Then, defining the vectors e and f as $\{e_0, e_1\}$ and $\{\overline{f^1(t)}/\sqrt{\lambda^1}, 1/\sqrt{\lambda^{01}}\}$, respectively, we may reformulate our problem as follows: To minimize (e, e) subject to the constraint $(e, f) = 1$. Expressing e as the sum of vectors g and h, where g is a multiple of f and h is orthogonal to g (the possibility of which is assured by the projection theorem, or by a trivial algebraic argument), we see that $(e, e) = (g, g) + (h, h)$ and that $(g, f) = (e, f) = 1$. Thus, if h is not the zero vector, e cannot possess the minimum norm consistent with the constraint $(e, f) = 1$. Therefore, e must reduce to a multiple of f, say $e = \gamma f$, and the constraint now takes the form $(\gamma f, f) = 1$, or $\gamma = (f, f)^{-1}$. We then find that $(e, e) = (\gamma f, \gamma f) = (f, f)^{-1}$; noting that $(e, e) = \lambda^{*1}$, we obtain $\lambda^{*1} = (f, f)^{-1}$, or

$$\lambda^{*1} = \gamma = \left[\frac{|f^{1\prime}(t)|^2}{\lambda^1} + \frac{1}{\lambda^{01}} \right]^{-1}. \tag{3-31}$$

The condition $e = \gamma f$ may be written in the form

$$d_0 = \frac{\gamma \overline{f^{1\prime}(t)}}{\lambda^1}, \qquad d_1 = \frac{\gamma}{\lambda^{01}}. \tag{3-32}$$

Taking account of (3-31), we now can write down an explicit expression for the extremal function $f^{*1}(z)$.

Without going into further detail, we remark that essentially the same procedure may be applied when two or more conditions are omitted. The simplest example of such a case is presented in Problem 3-9.

It is noteworthy that (3-31) immediately furnishes the inequality

$$\lambda^{*1} \leqslant \lambda^{01}. \tag{3-33}$$

This result can be established without computation by the following simple, yet often far-reaching, principle of a very general character. If two (solvable) minimization problems, say P_1 and P_2, are formulated, and if all the objects (usually, but not necessarily, functions of a certain class) that "compete" in problem P_1 also "compete" in problem P_2, then the minimum for problem P_2 cannot exceed the minimum for problem P_1. In the present case, P_1 is the problem of minimizing $\|f\|^2$ under the *two* constraints $f(t) = 0$, $f'(t) = 1$, whereas P_2 is the problem of minimizing $\|f\|^2$ under the latter constraint only. It is evident that the above principle is applicable, and (3-33) is simply the assertion of this principle.

PROBLEM

3-9. Determine the function f^{**1} and the corresponding number λ^{**1}.

¶ **3-8** Although the basis developed in Section 3-6 was seen in Section 3-7 to be especially convenient for solving certain extremal problems, it appears plausible that the formulas obtained for the extremal functions and the corresponding λ's can be converted into forms that make no reference to the choice of a particular, or "preferred," basis. We shall indicate how this can be accomplished, but for simplicity in exposition we shall confine ourselves to the single problem of determining $f^{\alpha_0 \alpha_1}$ and $\lambda^{\alpha_0 \alpha_1}$. We shall have occasion in this and later sections to employ a procedure of "complex differentiation," and the reader unacquainted with this subject is referred to the brief treatment that is provided in the Appendix.

Referring to the expansion (3-21) and replacing τ by z, we immediately obtain

$$K(z, z) = \frac{f^1(z)\overline{f^1(z)}}{\lambda^1} + \frac{f^{01}(z)\overline{f^{01}(z)}}{\lambda^{01}} + \cdots. \qquad (3\text{-}34)$$

First, setting $z = t$ and recalling that $f^1(t) = 1$, $f^{01}(t) = f^{001}(t) = \cdots = 0$, we obtain again the fact that $K(t, t) = 1/\lambda^1$. Next, differentiating (3-34) with respect to z and then setting $z = t$, we obtain $K_z(t, t) = f^{1'}(t)/\lambda^1$. Similarly, $K_{\bar{z}}(t, t) = \overline{f^{1'}(t)}/\lambda^1$ and $K_{z\bar{z}}(t, t) = |f^{1'}(t)|^2/\lambda^1 + 1/\lambda^{01}$. Substituting these results into (3-25) and performing a little algebraic manipulation, we obtain

$$\lambda^{\alpha_0 \alpha_1} = \frac{|\alpha_0|^2}{K} + \frac{|\alpha_1 K - \alpha_0 K_z|^2}{K(KK_{z\bar{z}} - K_z K_{\bar{z}})}, \qquad (3\text{-}35)$$

where the quantities K, K_z, $K_{\bar{z}}$, and $K_{z\bar{z}}$ are all evaluated for $z = t$. This result may be converted into the quotient of two determinants:

$$\lambda^{\alpha_0 \alpha_1} = -\frac{\begin{vmatrix} 0 & \bar{\alpha}_0 & \bar{\alpha}_1 \\ \alpha_0 & K & K_{\bar{z}} \\ \alpha_1 & K_z & K_{z\bar{z}} \end{vmatrix}}{\begin{vmatrix} K & K_{\bar{z}} \\ K_z & K_{z\bar{z}} \end{vmatrix}}. \qquad (3\text{-}36)$$

In particular, we get the following result, which will be useful in Chapter 4:

$$\lambda^{01} = \frac{K}{KK_{z\bar{z}} - K_z K_{\bar{z}}}. \qquad (3\text{-}37)$$

In very much the same way, we obtain an explicit expression for $f^{\alpha_0 \alpha_1}$, and in particular for f^{01}. Referring to (3-21), we easily obtain the following results: $f^1(z) = K(z, t)/K(t, t)$ (already known), $f^{1'}(t) = K_z(t, t)/K(t, t)$, and

$$f^{01}(z) = \lambda^{01}[K_{\bar{t}}(z, t)K(t, t) - K_z(t, t)K(z, t)]/K(t, t).$$

After replacing λ^{01} in the last result by the right side of (3-37) we have all the information needed to express $f^{\alpha_0 \alpha_1}$, as given in (3-23), in terms of α_0, α_1, $K(z, t)$, $K(t, t)$, $K_z(t, t)$, $K_{\bar{z}}(t, t)$, $K_{z\bar{z}}(t, t)$, and $K_{\bar{z}}(z, t)$. The final result is given by the formula

$$
f^{\alpha_0 \alpha_1}(z) = - \frac{\begin{vmatrix} 0 & K(z, t) & K_{\bar{z}}(z, t) \\ \alpha_0 & K & K_{\bar{z}} \\ \alpha_1 & K_z & K_{z\bar{z}} \end{vmatrix}}{\begin{vmatrix} K & K_{\bar{z}} \\ K_z & K_{z\bar{z}} \end{vmatrix}}.
\tag{3-38}
$$

In particular, setting $\alpha_0 = 0$, $\alpha_1 = 1$, we obtain

$$
f^{01}(z) = \frac{K K_{\bar{z}}(z, t) - K(z, t) K_{\bar{z}}}{K K_{z\bar{z}} - K_z K_{\bar{z}}}.
\tag{3-39}
$$

We emphasize that where the arguments are not shown explicitly, both variables are to be assigned the value t.

PROBLEM

3-10. Work out (3-36), (3-37), (3-38), and (3-39) in detail for the unit disc.

¶ **3-9** Let the domain D be a subset of the domain $\tilde{D}$, and let t be any point contained in D. Then any minimal problem of the type discussed in Sections 3-7 and 3-8 may be solved twice, once within the space $\mathscr{L}_2(D)$ and once within the space $\mathscr{L}_2(\tilde{D})$. If we denote the extremal functions as $f_D{}^{\cdots}$ and $f_{\tilde{D}}{}^{\cdots}$, and their respective squared norms as $\lambda_D{}^{\cdots}$ and $\lambda_{\tilde{D}}{}^{\cdots}$, we immediately observe that

$$
\lambda_{\tilde{D}}{}^{\cdots} = \iint_{\tilde{D}} |f_{\tilde{D}}{}^{\cdots}|^2 \, dx \, dy \geqslant \iint_D |f_{\tilde{D}}{}^{\cdots}|^2 \, dx \, dy.
$$

Since $f_{\tilde{D}}{}^{\cdots}$ (or, more precisely, the restriction of $f_{\tilde{D}}{}^{\cdots}$ to the domain D) is one of the "competing" functions involved in determining $f_D{}^{\cdots}$, it follows that the latter integral cannot be less than $\lambda_D{}^{\cdots}$. Thus, we obtain the inequality

$$
\lambda_{\tilde{D}}{}^{\cdots} \geqslant \lambda_D{}^{\cdots}.
\tag{3-40}
$$

Thus, we have the "principle of the minimum integral:"

Any extremal quantity $\lambda_D{}^{\cdots}$ increases monotonely as the domain D increases.

This result will be applied several times in Chapter 4. Here we simply mention the inequality

$$K_{\tilde{D}}(t, t) \leqslant K_D(t, t), \tag{3-41}$$

which follows from (3-40) by choosing λ^1 for $\lambda^{...}$ and taking account of the equality $\lambda^1 = (K(t, t))^{-1}$. Thus, $K_D(t, t)$ *decreases* monotonely as the domain D expands.

¶ **3-10**   We conclude this chapter with an application of orthogonal functions to the problem of analytic continuation. Given a function $f(z)$ defined and analytic in a domain D, it is often of interest to determine whether $f(z)$ can be "analytically continued" to a domain $\tilde{D}$ that contains D—i.e., whether there exists a function $f(z)$ analytic in $\tilde{D}$ and coinciding in D with $f(z)$. In principle this problem can be solved by beginning with the Taylor series expansion of $f(z)$ about some point z_0 in D, reexpanding this series about some point other than z_0, inside the disc within which the series converges, and then repeating this procedure appropriately. If by means of a finite number or infinite sequence of reexpansions the domain $\tilde{D}$ has been covered with the "discs of convergence," we may consider the original function to have been continued analytically to $\tilde{D}$. (We refrain from discussing a complicating factor that can occur if $\tilde{D}$ is multiply connected—namely, that different values of $f(z)$ may be obtained at some or all points of $\tilde{D}$.) In contrast to this procedure, which is rarely practicable in specific cases, we shall show how it is possible by means of *one* series expansion to determine whether $f(z)$ can be continued to $\tilde{D}$; however, we must impose the additional restriction that $f(z)$, when continued to $\tilde{D}$, shall belong to $\mathscr{L}_2(\tilde{D})$.

Let t be any point of D, and let the functions $f^1(z), f^{01}(z), f^{001}(z), \ldots$ associated with the point t and the domain $\tilde{D}$ (*not* the domain D) be given. Then, if $f(z)$ can be continued analytically to all of $\tilde{D}$, the continuation, which we also denote by $f(z)$, is unique, and the extended function belongs to $\mathscr{L}_2(\tilde{D})$ if and only if the coefficients $c_0, c_1, c_2, \ldots$ appearing in the expansion

$$f(z) = c_0 f^1(z) + c_1 f^{01}(z) + c_2 f^{001}(z) + \cdots \tag{3-42}$$

are such that the series

$$|c_0|^2 \lambda^1 + |c_1|^2 \lambda^{01} + |c_2|^2 \lambda^{001} + \cdots$$

converges. Conversely, if coefficients $c_0, c_1, c_2, \ldots$ exist such that this series converges and such that the series (3-42) converges to

$f(z)$ everywhere in D (in fact, in any nonempty open subset of D), then the series (3-42) converges *throughout* $\tilde{D}$ to a function $f(z)$, which evidently constitutes an analytic continuation of $f(z)$ from D to $\tilde{D}$.

Now, setting $z = t$ on both sides of (3-42), we see that $c_0 = f(t)$. Differentiating both sides of (3-42) and then setting $z = t$, we obtain $c_1 = f'(t) - c_0 f^{1'}(t)$; similarly, all the later coefficients appearing in (3-42) are determined unambiguously in terms of the quantities $f(t), f'(t), f''(t), \ldots$. Thus, in particular, the coefficients appearing in (3-42) can be determined from the coefficients of the Taylor expansion of $f(z)$ about the point t and from a knowledge of the functions $f^1(z), f^{01}(z), \ldots$. In this way we see that, once the functions $f^1(z), f^{01}(z), \ldots$ are known, the possibility of continuing $f(z)$ from D to $\tilde{D}$ as an analytic function quadratically integrable over $\tilde{D}$ is settled completely by determining the convergence or divergence of the series following (3-42).

4

Conformal Mapping

¶ **4-1** In this chapter we shall discuss several applications of the reproducing kernel to problems of conformal mapping. We begin by considering the case of a simply connected domain.

The Riemann Mapping Theorem asserts that every simply connected domain D in the extended complex plane that possesses at least two boundary points (and hence, in particular, any *bounded* domain) can be mapped conformally and one-to-one onto the unit disc; furthermore, a prescribed point t in D may be made to map into the origin, and the angle of rotation at t—i.e., the argument of the derivative of the mapping function—may also be prescribed. With these conditions, the mapping function is uniquely determined. We may formulate this theorem in analytical terms by asserting that there exists a unique function $f(z)$ which is analytic in D and satisfies the following conditions:

(a) $|f(z)| < 1$ everywhere in D.

(b) For each α, $|\alpha| < 1$, the equation $f(z) = \alpha$ possesses a unique solution in D.

(c) $f(t) = 0$, t being a specified point of D.

(d) $\arg f'(t) = \theta$, θ being a specified real number.

We shall now show that the mapping function $f(z)$ is very closely related to the reproducing kernel of the domain D (with parameter point t).

¶ 4-2 Let G be a bounded domain in the complex plane whose boundary, which we denote as Γ, consists of a finite number of smooth, simple, closed curves, and let $g(z)$ and $h(z)$ be any two functions that are analytic inside and on Γ. Then, as is proved in the Appendix,

$$\int\int_G g(z)\overline{h'(z)}\, dx\, dy = -\frac{i}{2}\int_\Gamma g\bar{h}\, dz. \qquad (4\text{-}1)$$

Now let D be any bounded simply connected domain, let $f(z)$ be the mapping function defined in the preceding section, and let G_r be that part of D that is mapped by $w = f(z)$ onto the (open) disc $|w| < r$, r being some positive number less than unity. Also, let $g(z)$ be any function belonging to $\mathcal{L}_2(D)$ and let Γ_r be the boundary of G_r. Choosing $f(z)$ as the function $h(z)$ introduced previously, we obtain

$$\int\int_{G_r} g(z)\,\overline{f'(z)}\, dx\, dy = -\frac{i}{2}\int_{\Gamma_r} g\bar{f}\, dz. \qquad (4\text{-}2)$$

Now, from the definition of G_r it follows that $|f(z)|^2 \equiv r^2$ for z on Γ_r, and so (4-2) may be rewritten in the following form:

$$\int\int_{G_r} g(z)\,\overline{f'(z)}\, dx\, dy = -\frac{ir^2}{2}\int_{\Gamma_r} \frac{g(z)}{f(z)}\, dz. \qquad (4\text{-}3)$$

Since $f(z)$ possesses a simple zero at the point t, which is inside Γ_r, the right side of (4-3) is easily found (by a residue calculation) to have the value $\pi r^2 g(t)/f'(t)$. If we now let r approach unity, the left side of (4-3) approaches the integral $\int\int_D g(z)\,\overline{f'(z)}\, dx\, dy$, whereas the right side approaches $\pi g(t)/f'(t)$. Thus,

$$\frac{\pi g(t)}{f'(t)} = (g, f'), \qquad (4\text{-}4)$$

or

$$g(t) = \left(g, \frac{\overline{f'(t)}}{\pi} f'\right). \qquad (4\text{-}5)$$

We have, therefore, shown that the function $\overline{f'(t)}f'(z)/\pi$ possesses the reproducing property that *characterizes* the kernel $K(z, t)$. Therefore,

$$\overline{f'(t)}f'(z) = \pi K(z, t). \tag{4-6}$$

If we replace z in (4-6) by t and extract the positive square root of both sides, we obtain

$$|f'(t)| = (\pi K(t, t))^{1/2}. \tag{4-7}$$

Since $\arg f'(t) = \theta$, we immediately obtain

$$f'(t) = e^{i\theta} (\pi K(t, t))^{1/2}. \tag{4-8}$$

We now immediately obtain from (4-6) the following striking relationship between the mapping function $f(z)$ and the reproducing kernel $K(z, t)$:

$$f'(z) = e^{i\theta}\left(\frac{\pi}{K(t, t)}\right)^{1/2} K(z, t). \tag{4-9}$$

By integration we immediately obtain the formula

$$f(z) = e^{i\theta}\left(\frac{\pi}{K(t, t)}\right)^{1/2} \int_t^z K(\zeta, t)\, d\zeta. \tag{4-10}$$

¶ **4-3**   The formula (4-9) enables us to obtain a second proof of the formula (3-12) for the kernel of the unit disc. The function mapping the unit disc conformally onto itself and sending the point t into the origin with angle of rotation θ is given by

$$f(z) = e^{i\theta}\frac{z - t}{1 - \bar{t}z}. \tag{4-11}$$

Differentiating with respect to z and substituting into (4-9), we obtain

$$e^{i\theta}\frac{1 - |t|^2}{(1 - \bar{t}z)^2} = e^{i\theta}\left(\frac{\pi}{K(t, t)}\right)^{1/2} K(z, t). \tag{4-12}$$

Setting $z = t$ we now obtain

$$\frac{1}{1 - |t|^2} = (\pi K(t, t))^{1/2}. \tag{4-13}$$

It follows that

$$K(t, t) = \frac{1}{\pi(1 - |t|^2)^2}. \tag{4-14}$$

Substituting this expression for $K(t, t)$ into (4-12), we now obtain, in agreement with (3-12):

$$K(z, t) = \frac{1}{\pi(1 - z\bar{t})^2}. \tag{4-15}$$

Conversely, if we substitute from (4-15) into (4-10) and perform the indicated integration, we obtain (4-11).

¶ 4-4 In the following section we shall present a second derivation of the equation (4-9). For this purpose we shall need a formula indicating how the reproducing kernels of two conformally equivalent domains are related to each other.

Let the bounded domain D (not necessarily simply connected), lying in the z-plane, be mapped conformally and one-to-one onto the bounded domain $\tilde{D}$, lying in the w-plane, by the mapping $w = f(z)$. It is readily seen that a one-to-one correspondence can be established between the functions in $\mathscr{L}_2(D)$ and those in $\mathscr{L}_2(\tilde{D})$ as follows:

$$g(w) \leftrightarrow g(f(z))f'(z). \tag{4-16}$$

Furthermore, this correspondence preserves inner products; by this we mean that if $g_1(w)$ and $g_2(w)$ are any two functions in $\mathscr{L}_2(\tilde{D})$ and if $G_1(z)$ and $G_2(z)$ are the corresponding functions in $\mathscr{L}_2(D)$, then

$$\iint_{\tilde{D}} g_1(w)\overline{g_2(w)}\, du\, dv = \iint_D G_1(z)\overline{G_2(z)}\, dx\, dy. \tag{4-17}$$

The proof of this assertion, which is based on the role of the Jacobian in the transformation of multiple integrals, is left to the reader as Problem 4-1. In particular, if the functions $\{\psi_n(w)\}$ constitute an orthonormal basis in $\mathscr{L}_2(\tilde{D})$, then the functions $\{\phi_n(z)\}$, where $\phi_n(z) = \psi_n(f(z))f'(z)$, constitute an orthonormal basis in $\mathscr{L}_2(D)$. Taking account twice of the expansion of the kernel in terms of an arbitrary orthonormal basis, we obtain

$$K_D(z, t) = \sum_{n=1}^{\infty} \phi_n(z)\overline{\phi_n(t)} = \sum_{n=1}^{\infty} \psi_n(w)\overline{\psi_n(\tau)}f'(z)\overline{f'(t)}$$
$$= K_{\tilde{D}}(w, \tau)f'(z)\overline{f'(t)}, \tag{4-18}$$

where, of course, $\tau = f(t)$. This is the desired transformation formula.

To illustrate (4-18), suppose, in particular, that both D and $\tilde{D}$ are chosen as the unit disc. The reasoning employed in Section 1-2 shows that the problem of minimizing $\iint |g|^2\, dx\, dy$ with the restriction

$g(0) = 1$ is solved by the function $g(z) \equiv 1$, and the minimum of this integral is equal to π. Hence, $K(0, 0) = 1/\pi$ and $K(z, 0)/K(0, 0) \equiv 1$. Thus, $K(z, 0) \equiv 1/\pi$. Now let the unit disc be mapped conformally onto itself by the linear transformation

$$w = f(z) = \frac{z + \tau}{1 + \bar{\tau}z}. \tag{4-19}$$

A simple calculation shows that (4-18) assumes, in this case, the form

$$\frac{1}{\pi} = K(w, \tau)\frac{(1 - |\tau|^2)^2}{(1 + \bar{\tau}z)^2}. \tag{4-20}$$

Solving for $K(w, \tau)$ and expressing z in terms of w [from (4-19)] we obtain, in agreement with two previous derivations, the following formula for the reproducing kernel of the unit disc:

$$K(w, \tau) = \frac{1}{\pi(1 - \bar{\tau}w)^2}. \tag{4-21}$$

PROBLEMS

4-1. Prove (4-17).

4-2. Work out the details leading to (4-21).

¶ **4-5** We now obtain a second proof of (4-9) as follows. Let D and $\tilde{D}$ be any two bounded simply connected domains, and let $w = f(z)$ map D conformally onto $\tilde{D}$, and let $f(t) = \tau$, $\arg f'(t) = \theta$. Then, taking account of (4-18), we obtain

$$f'(z) - e^{i\theta}\left(\frac{\pi}{K_D(t, t)}\right)^{1/2}K_D(z, t)$$

$$= f'(z)\left[1 - e^{i\theta}\left(\frac{\pi}{K_{\tilde{D}}(\tau, \tau)|f'(t)|^2}\right)^{1/2}K_{\tilde{D}}(w, \tau)\overline{f'(t)}\right]. \tag{4-22}$$

If $\tilde{D}$ is the unit disc and τ is the origin, then, as we see from (4-21), both $K_{\tilde{D}}(w, \tau)$ and $K_{\tilde{D}}(\tau, \tau)$ reduce to $1/\pi$. and then the right side of (4-22) reduces to $f'(z)[1 - e^{i\theta}\overline{f'(t)}/|f'(t)|]$, or 0. Thus, the left side of (4-22) must vanish, and so, in agreement with (4-9), we obtain

$$f'(z) = e^{i\theta}\left(\frac{\pi}{K_D(t, t)}\right)^{1/2}K_D(z, t).$$

¶ **4-6** If $f(z)$ is any function that is analytic in a simply connected domain D, then the value of the integral $\int\int_D |f'(z)|^2\, dx\, dy$ equals the area of the image of D; however, if $f(z)$ is not one-to-one, the image of D must be considered to consist of an appropriate Riemann surface rather than a plane domain, so that points that are images of more than one point of D may be counted the correct number of times. From the discussion in Section 3-3 it follows that, if the function $f(z)$ is required to satisfy the condition $|f'(t)| = 1$, where t is some specified point of D, then the area of the image of D cannot be less than $1/K(t, t)$. Equality is attained if and only if $f'(z)$ is of the form $e^{i\theta}K(z, t)$, where θ is an arbitrary real constant, and we have seen that when this condition is satisfied, $f(z)$ must map the domain D in a one-to-one manner onto a disc. It is of interest that the extremal functions turn out to be univalent (one-to-one), although this condition is not imposed in advance. However, it should be noted that the single-valuedness of $\int_t^z K(\zeta, t)\, d\zeta$ follows from the Cauchy integral theorem, since D is assumed to be simply connected.

If D is multiply connected, the above argument breaks down, for, as is shown in Problem 4-3, the integral $\int_t^z K(\zeta, t)\, d\zeta$ may fail to be single valued.

PROBLEM

4-3. Let D be the annulus $0 < r < |z| < 1$. Prove that $\int_t^z K(\zeta, t)\, d\zeta$ is not single valued. *Hint:* The function $1/z$ belongs to $\mathscr{L}_2(D)$ but does not possess a single-valued integral. (More generally, this result evidently holds for any multiply connected domain having at least two simple closed curves among its boundary components.)

¶ **4-7** Within the space $\mathscr{L}_2(D)$ associated with a multiply connected domain D let us confine attention to those functions that possess a single-valued integral. As shown in Problem 4-3, these functions constitute a *proper* subset of $\mathscr{L}_2(D)$ (under mild hypotheses on the boundary of D). We denote this subset $\mathscr{L}_{2,s}(D)$, the additional subscript serving to indicate the restriction to functions possessing single-valued integrals. $\mathscr{L}_{2,s}(D)$ is evidently a linear manifold of $\mathscr{L}_2(D)$, for any finite linear combination of functions possessing single-valued integrals also possesses a single-valued integral.

Furthermore, $\mathscr{L}_{2,s}(D)$ is a closed subset of $\mathscr{L}_2(D)$, for if the sequence $\{f_n(z)\}$ of functions belonging to $\mathscr{L}_{2,s}(D)$ converges in norm to $f(z)$, these functions converge *uniformly* to $f(z)$ on any closed curve Γ lying in D, so that $\int_\Gamma f(z)\, dz = \lim_{n \to \infty} \int_\Gamma f_n(z)\, dz = 0$. Therefore, $\mathscr{L}_{2,s}(D)$ is itself a Hilbert space [with the same definition of inner product as is employed in $\mathscr{L}_2(D)$—namely $(f, g) = \int\int_D f\bar{g}\, dx\, dy$]. Since $f(t)$ is, for fixed t in D, a bounded linear functional in $\mathscr{L}_2(D)$, it is also a bounded linear functional in $\mathscr{L}_{2,s}(D)$, and so it follows that $\mathscr{L}_{2,s}(D)$ possesses a reproducing kernel, $K^{(s)}(z, t)$, such that, for any function $f(z)$ in $\mathscr{L}_{2,s}(D)$ and any point t in D,

$$f(t) = (f, K^{(s)}(z, t)) = \int\int_D f(z)\overline{K^{(s)}(z, t)}\, dx\, dy \qquad (4\text{-}23)$$

Similarly, the function $K^{(s)}(z, t)/K^{(s)}(t, t)$ minimizes $\|f\|^2$ among all functions in $\mathscr{L}_{2,s}(D)$ that assume the value unity at t, and the minimum is equal to $1/K^{(s)}(t, t)$.

More generally, it is evident that with each subspace S of $\mathscr{L}_2(D)$ we can associate a reproducing kernel and that this kernel possesses the bilinear expansion (3-20) in terms of any orthonormal basis $\{\phi_n(z)\}$ for the subspace S. Also, minimum problems of the type discussed in Chapter 3 may be solved within S, with the aid of the reproducing kernel of S, exactly as was indicated for the entire space $\mathscr{L}_2(D)$.

PROBLEMS

4-4. Prove that $K^{(s)}(t, t) \leqslant K(t, t)$. *Hint:* Take account of the interpretation of $1/K^{(s)}(t, t)$ and $1/K(t, t)$ as minima of certain integrals.

4-5. Let S_1 and S_2 be closed linear manifolds of $\mathscr{L}_2(D)$, and let $S_1 \subset S_2$. Then prove that their respective reproducing kernels, $K_1(z, t)$ and $K_2(z, t)$, satisfy the inequality $K_1(t, t) \leqslant K_2(t, t)$.

4-6. Let S be any subspace of $\mathscr{L}_2(D)$. The reproducing kernels of S, $S^\perp$, and $\mathscr{L}_2(D)$ are denoted by $K_1(z, t)$, $K_2(z, t)$, and $K(z, t)$, respectively. Prove that

$$K_1(z, t) + K_2(z, t) = K(z, t).$$

¶ **4-8** The following theorem constitutes a simple, yet interesting, application of the relationship (4-9) between the kernel function of a simply connected domain and the function that maps it conformally onto a disc:

Let D be a bounded* simply connected domain and let t be a point of D such that, for every function u(z) that is harmonic in D and integrable over D, the mean value of u equals u(t)—that is to say,

$$u(t) = A^{-1} \int \int_D u(z) \, dx \, dy, \qquad (4\text{-}24)$$

where A denotes the area of D. Then D is a disc with center at t.

We begin the proof by observing that if $f(z)$ belongs to $C_2(D)$, the integral $\int \int_D f(z) \, dx \, dy$ exists, for this integral is dominated by

$$\left(\int \int_D 1^2 \, dx \, dy \right)^{1/2} \left(\int \int_D |f|^2 \, dx \, dy \right)^{1/2}.$$

If $f(z)$ belongs to $\mathscr{L}_2(D)$, it is harmonic in D and integrable over D. According to the hypothesis, the equality

$$f(t) = A^{-1} \int \int_D f(z) \, dx \, dy \qquad (4\text{-}25)$$

must hold for every function $f(z)$ in $\mathscr{L}_2(D)$. We rewrite (4-25) in the form†

$$f(t) = \int \int_D f(z) \overline{A^{-1}} \, dx \, dy. \qquad (4\text{-}26)$$

Comparing this with (3-3) and recalling that $K(z, t)$ is *uniquely* determined in $\mathscr{L}_2(D)$ by its reproducing property, we see that

$$K(z, t) = A^{-1}, \qquad (4\text{-}27)$$

and hence that

$$\int_t^z K(\zeta, t) \, d\zeta = A^{-1}(z - t). \qquad (4\text{-}28)$$

Since D is assumed to be simply connected, the left side of (4-28), and hence $A^{-1}(z - t)$, maps D onto a disc with center at the origin. From this it is evident that D must be a disc with center at t, as was to be proven.

¶ **4-9** If we identify t with z and τ with w in (4-18) and express $f'(z)$ as the quotient of the differentials dw and dz, we obtain the following completely symmetric relationship between $K_D(z, z)$ and $K_{\tilde{D}}(w, w)$:

$$K_D(z, z) \, |dz|^2 = K_{\tilde{D}}(w, w) \, |dw|^2. \qquad (4\text{-}29)$$

---

* This restriction is unnecessary, but is included here since, for simplicity in exposition, we have restricted attention to bounded domains. It suffices to replace the condition of boundedness by the milder one that D should possess finite area.

† Since A is real, the conjugate sign may be inserted.

Let us define a "generalized length" of the curve Γ in D and its image $\tilde{\Gamma}$ in $\tilde{D}$ by the integrals $\int_\Gamma (K_D(z, z))^{1/2} |dz|$ and $\int_{\tilde{\Gamma}} (K_{\tilde{D}}(w, w))^{1/2} |dw|$, respectively. From (4-29) we see that this generalized length remains invariant (under conformal mapping), whereas the *Euclidean* length is, in general, altered. (Note that the generalized length depends not only upon the curve itself but also upon the domain in which it is considered to lie.) We have thus defined a *conformally invariant* length for each (sufficiently smooth) curve in a given domain D.

The reader acquainted with the basic concepts of differential geometry will recognize that the expression $K_D(z, z) |dz|^2$, or $K_D(z, z)[(dx)^2 + (dy)^2]$, defines a *Riemannian metric* on the domain D. Although one usually thinks of such a metric as describing, on a surface embedded in three-dimensional Euclidean space, the geometry induced by the latter space (the "ambient" space), it is entirely possible to confine attention entirely to domains in the z-plane, with the Euclidean length replaced by the aforementioned conformally invariant length. When this is done, all conformally equivalent plane domains become merely different concrete "realizations" of the same abstract geometrical structure—a *Riemannian manifold*.

In the remaining sections of this chapter we shall discuss briefly some topics related to the conformally invariant length which has just been introduced.

¶ 4-10 Let P be any point on a (sufficiently smooth) surface S embedded in Euclidean three-space. By a "normal section" at P we mean the intersection of S with a plane containing the normal to S at P. The curvatures of the various normal sections at P will, in general, vary; an exception occurs, for example, if P is any point on a sphere or either end of an ellipsoid of revolution. The product of the largest and smallest curvatures (due regard should be paid to the sign of the curvature, so that at a "saddle point" the curvature assumes both positive and negative values) is termed the *Gaussian curvature* of the surface S at P. If the surface S is deformed in the vicinity of P *without altering lengths of curves* on S—e.g., if S is a plane it may be deformed into a cylinder—the maximum and minimum curvatures of the normal sections at S will, in general, be altered, but a very remarkable theorem (Gauss' *theorema egregium*) asserts that the Gaussian curvature is left unaltered. We may thus assert that the Gaussian curvature at each point of S is completely and "intrinsically" determined by the measurement of lengths *on the surface*, without regard to the relationship between S and the ambient Euclidean space. In particular, when each curve in the domain D is assigned the conformally invariant length defined in the preceding section, the Gaussian curvature, which will be denoted by C, is given by the formula

$$C(t) = \frac{KK_{z\bar{z}} - K_z K_{\bar{z}}}{K^3}\Bigg]_{z=t}, \qquad K = K(z, z). \tag{4-30}$$

We shall now establish the striking fact that C can be expressed in terms of two "minimum integrals," the quantities λ^1 and λ^{01} defined in Section 3-6. Let us select any point t in the domain F and then determine the functions $f^1, f^{01}, \ldots$ and the quantities λ^1, $\lambda^{01}, \ldots$ associated with the point t. If we express $K(z, z)$ by replacing τ in (3-21) by z, we find easily that, at the point t, the quantities $K(z, z)$, $K_z(z, z)$, $K_{\bar{z}}(z, z)$, and $K_{z\bar{z}}(z, z)$ assume the following simple forms:

$$K(z, z) = \frac{1}{\lambda^1}, \qquad K_z(z, z) = \frac{f^{1\prime}(t)}{\lambda^1},$$

$$K_{\bar{z}}(z, z) = \frac{\overline{f^{1\prime}(t)}}{\lambda^1}, \qquad K_{z\bar{z}}(z, z) = \frac{|f^{1\prime}(t)|^2}{\lambda^1} + \frac{1}{\lambda^{01}}. \tag{4-31}$$

Substituting from (4-31) into (4-30), we immediately obtain for the Gaussian curvature the formula

$$C(t) = \frac{-2(\lambda^1)^2}{\lambda^{01}}. \tag{4-32}$$

Although (4-32) can be obtained directly from (4-30) without using the particular expansion (3-21) for the kernel function, it is evident that the use of this expansion greatly facilitates the proof of (4-32).

¶ 4-11   Since the Gaussian curvature is invariant under conformal mapping, it follows from the Riemann mapping theorem that this quantity must reduce to some universal constant—i.e., depending neither upon the particular domain nor upon the point at which it is evaluated—throughout any bounded simply connected domain. In order to evaluate this universal constant, it therefore suffices to evaluate the quantities λ^1 and λ^{01} in any one case that happens to lend itself easily to computation. The most obvious choice, is, of course, to choose the unit disc as the domain and to evaluate the aforementioned λ's at the origin. In this case, as we have already seen, λ^1 assumes the value π, whereas λ^{01} is easily found to be equal to $\pi/2$. Hence, the curvature is found to have the value -4π, at all *points of every bounded simply connected domain.*

We shall see later, by a specific computation, that the curvature is *not* constant in a doubly connected domain, but that, on the other hand, the curvature in any multiply connected domain approaches the aforementioned value of -4π as the point under consideration approaches any boundary point in whose vicinity the boundary satisfies certain mild restrictions. Before entering into a discussion of these matters, however, we shall discuss some interesting aspects of the Riemannian geometry defined in any simply connected domain by the invariant metric $K(z, z) \, |dz|^2$.

¶ **4-12** First, let us consider the invariant metric defined in the unit disc—namely

$$(ds)^2 = \frac{|dz|^2}{\pi(1 - |z|^2)^2}.$$

Either by exploiting the rotational symmetry of the quantity $\sqrt{\pi}(1 - |z|^2)$, which furnishes the ratio of Euclidean to invariant arc length, or by a routine application of the Euler-Lagrange equations of the calculus of variations, we immediately see that there exists a unique shortest curve connecting the origin to any other point ζ in the disc—namely, the straight-line segment joining these two points. Furthermore, the invariant length of this segment—i.e., the "minimal distance" or "geodesic distance"—is given by the integral

$$\int_0^{|\zeta|} \frac{dr}{\pi^{1/2}(1 - r^2)},$$

which is easily evaluated, furnishing the value

$$\tfrac{1}{2}\pi^{-1/2} \log \left[(1 + |\zeta|)/(1 - |\zeta|)\right].$$

Letting $|\zeta|$ approach unity, we see that the boundary is, so to speak, infinitely far from the origin (and from any other point of the disc).

Now let us consider any two distinct points ζ_1 and ζ_2 in the disc, and let us seek to determine the shortest curve connecting these two points; by "shortest" we mean, of course, that its *invariant* length is to be as small as possible. Let us perform the linear transformation

$$w = \frac{z - \zeta_1}{1 - \bar{\zeta}_1 z}, \tag{4-33}$$

which maps the unit disc onto itself and maps the points ζ_1 and ζ_2 into the origin and $(\zeta_2 - \zeta_1)/(1 - \bar{\zeta}_1\zeta_2)$, respectively. Recalling the result of the previous paragraph, we find that the length of the shortest curve connecting the two given points is equal to

$$\tfrac{1}{2}\pi^{-1/2} \log \frac{|1 - \bar{\zeta}_1\zeta_2| + |\zeta_2 - \zeta_1|}{|1 - \bar{\zeta}_1\zeta_2| - |\zeta_2 - \zeta_1|}.$$

Furthermore, the unique curve joining ζ_1 and ζ_2 and possessing the above minimal length must be transformed by the mapping (4-33) into the line segment joining the origin to $(\zeta_2 - \zeta_1)/(1 - \bar{\zeta}_1\zeta_2)$. From the theory of linear transformations, we know that such a curve must be a circular arc,* and that the circle of which this arc constitutes a segment must intersect the unit circle orthogonally. Such circles are known as "oricycles" of the unit circle.

Just as two distinct points in the Euclidean plane can be joined by a unique line segment, we have seen that two distinct points in the unit disc can be joined by a unique segment of an oricycle, which provides the connection of minimal *invariant* length. On the other hand, we easily see that the parallel postulate of Euclidean geometry does *not* carry over to the geometry under discussion here. Let Γ be any oricycle, let Γ intersect the unit circle at z_1 and z_2, and let z_3 be any point in the unit disc not lying on Γ. Then there exist infinitely many oricycles that pass through z_3 and do not meet Γ. Indeed, let oricycle Γ_1 join z_1 and z_3, and similarly let the oricycle Γ_2 join z_2 and z_3. Let Γ_1 and Γ_2 meet the unit circle at z_1' and z_2', respectively. Then any oricycle through z_3 that terminates on the circular arcs $z_1 z_2'$ and $z_2 z_1'$ is parallel to Γ in the sense that these two oricycles do not meet within the space under consideration—namely, the disc. Of these infinitely many oricycles there are two (Γ_1 and Γ_2) that are parallel to Γ in a sense more restrictive than that in which the term "parallel" was used in the previous sentence, for these oricycles each meet the oricycle Γ "at infinity"—namely, on the circumference of the disc.

---

* If ζ_1 and ζ_2 are collinear with the origin, the curve becomes a line segment. As is usual in the theory of linear transformations, we consider lines as circles—namely, those circles that pass through the point at infinity.

¶ **4-13** We shall now prove the assertion made in Section 4-11 that the Gaussian curvature approaches the value -4π at the boundary of a multiply connected domain that satisfies mild hypotheses. Roughly speaking, this remarkable result asserts that, as the point ζ of the multiply connected domain D approaches a point lying on one of the boundary components of D, the *remaining* boundary components become more remote from ζ and exert a diminishing influence on the metrical coefficient $K(\zeta, \zeta)$ and its derivatives appearing in the computation of the curvature (or, equivalently, on the quantities λ^1 and λ^{01}). Thus, the invariant metric comes to resemble that of a simply connected domain.

First, let us consider the particular case of a bounded domain D of finite connectivity n whose outer boundary component is the unit circle. Given any positive number ϵ, we shall show that there exists a positive number δ such that, whenever the distance from the point ζ to the unit circle is less than δ—i.e., whenever $1 - \delta < |\zeta| < 1$—the inequality $|C + 4\pi| < \epsilon$ is satisfied. From the hypotheses we are assured that there exists a positive number α such that all points satisfying the inequality $1 - \alpha < |\zeta| < 1$ lie in D. Restricting ζ henceforth to satisfy the inequalities $1 - \alpha/2 < |\zeta| < 1$ and assuming, without loss of generality (for we may always perform a suitable rotation without affecting the reasoning), that ζ is real and positive, we introduce the discs $\tilde{D}$ and $\overset{\approx}{D}$ defined by the inequalities $|z - (1 - \alpha/2)| < \alpha/2$ and $|z| < 1$, respectively. Evidently the inclusion relationships $\zeta \in \tilde{D} \subset D \subset \overset{\approx}{D}$ are satisfied, and so, by the principle of the minimum integral (Section 3-9), the inequalities

$$\lambda_{\tilde{D}}^{1} \leqslant \lambda_{D}^{1} \leqslant \lambda_{\overset{\approx}{D}}^{1} \tag{4-34a}$$

and

$$\lambda_{\tilde{D}}^{01} \leqslant \lambda_{D}^{01} \leqslant \lambda_{\overset{\approx}{D}}^{01} \tag{4-34b}$$

are all satisfied at ζ. Since all the λ's are positive, we derive from (4-34a) and (4-34b) the further inequalities

$$(\lambda_{\tilde{D}}^{1})^2/\lambda_{\overset{\approx}{D}}^{01} \leqslant (\lambda_{D}^{1})^2/\lambda_{D}^{01} \leqslant (\lambda_{\overset{\approx}{D}}^{1})^2/\lambda_{\tilde{D}}^{01} \tag{4-35}$$

Now, the kernel functions of the domains $\tilde{D}$ and $\overset{\approx}{D}$ are given, respectively, by

$$K_{\tilde{D}}(z, t) = \frac{(\alpha/2)^2}{\pi[(\alpha/2)^2 - (z - 1 + \alpha/2)(\bar{t} - 1 + \alpha/2)]^2} \tag{4-36a}$$

and

$$K_{\overset{\approx}{D}}(z, t) = \frac{1}{\pi(1 - z\bar{t})^2}. \tag{4-36b}$$

By the method explained in Section 3-8 we readily obtain (recalling that $\zeta = \bar{\zeta}$):

$$\lambda_{\bar{D}}^{1}(\zeta) = \frac{\pi[(\alpha/2)^2 - (\zeta - 1 + \alpha/2)^2]^2}{(\alpha/2)^2}, \tag{4-37a}$$

$$\lambda_{\bar{D}}^{1}(\zeta) = \pi(1 - \zeta^2)^2, \tag{4-37b}$$

$$\lambda_{\bar{D}}^{01}(\zeta) = \frac{8\pi[(\alpha/2)^2 - (\zeta - 1 + \alpha/2)^2]^4}{\alpha^4}, \tag{4-37c}$$

$$\lambda_{\bar{D}}^{01}(\zeta) = \tfrac{1}{2}\pi(1 - \zeta^2)^4. \tag{4-37d}$$

The inequalities (4-35) now assume the form, after some elementary algebraic simplifications:

$$\frac{32\pi(\alpha + \zeta - 1)^4}{\alpha^4(1 + \zeta)^4} \leqslant (\lambda_D^{1})^2/\lambda_D^{01} \leqslant \frac{\pi\alpha^4(1 + \zeta)^4}{8(\alpha + \zeta - 1)^4}. \tag{4-38}$$

Now, letting ζ approach unity, we find that both extreme sides of (4-38), and hence the center expression, approach 2π; recalling that α is fixed, we immediately see that this is equivalent to the assertion that the curvature differs from -4π by less than the preassigned quantity ϵ at any point ζ of D whose modulus satisfies the inequalities $1 - \delta < |\zeta| < 1$, where δ depends only on ϵ (and the aforementioned quantity α).

Now, more generally, let D be any multiply connected domain of finite connectivity, and let Γ denote any boundary component that does not consist of a single point. The complement of Γ (with respect to the plane) consists of one or more open simply connected components, and the domain D (together with its other boundary components) must be contained in one of these components, say D_1. If we map D_1 conformally onto the unit disc, in accordance with the Riemann mapping theorem, D is mapped onto a portion of the disc, whereas the boundary components of D other than Γ, being closed sets, are mapped onto closed subsets of the unit disc. Thus, the image of D contains all points of the unit disc satisfying, for some sufficiently small positive number α, the inequality $|z| > 1 - \alpha$. Since the curvature is invariant under conformal mapping, we conclude, by invoking the previous argument and then returning to the domain D, that the Gaussian curvature approaches -4π as the boundary component Γ is approached.

¶ **4-14** The principle of the minimum integral played an essential role in the reasoning employed in Section 4-13. A second application of this principle, also possessing an interesting geometrical interpretation, is the following: Let two domains D and $\tilde{D}$ be given, let $\tilde{D}$ be contained in D, and let Γ be a curve contained in $\tilde{D}$. Then Γ may be assigned two different invariant lengths, once as a curve lying in D and once as a curve lying in $\tilde{D}$. These two lengths are given by the following integrals, respectively:

$$L_D = \int_\Gamma (K_D(z, z))^{1/2} |dz|, \qquad L_{\tilde{D}} = \int_\Gamma (K_{\tilde{D}}(z, z))^{1/2} |dz|. \qquad (4\text{-}39)$$

Since $K_D(z, z) = 1/\lambda_D{}^1(z)$ and $K_{\tilde{D}}(z, z) = 1/\lambda_{\tilde{D}}{}^1(z)$, it follows from the principle of the minimum integral that $K_{\tilde{D}}(z, z) \geqslant K_D(z, z)$, and hence that $L_{\tilde{D}} \geqslant L_D$. Thus, we may assert that as a domain shrinks, the invariant length of a curve lying in the domain increases.

As a particular example, of considerable interest in itself, we consider the case when D is the unit disc and $\tilde{D}$ is a subdomain of D which is the image of D under the one-to-one analytic mapping $w = f(z)$. A "linear element" possessing Euclidean length $|dz|$ is transformed into a "linear element" of Euclidean length $|dw|$, where $|dw| = |f'(z)| \cdot |dz|$, and their invariant lengths are equal—namely

$$K_D(z, z))^{1/2} |dz| = (K_{\tilde{D}}(w, w))^{1/2} |dw|. \qquad (4\text{-}40)$$

On the other hand, as explained in the previous paragraph,

$$(K_{\tilde{D}}(w, w))^{1/2} |dw| \geqslant (K_D(w, w))^{1/2} |dw|, \qquad (4\text{-}41)$$

and so

$$\left|\frac{dw}{dz}\right| \leqslant \left(\frac{K_D(z, z)}{K_D(w, w)}\right)^{1/2}. \qquad (4\text{-}42)$$

Recalling the explicit formula for the kernel of the unit disc, we find that (4-42) assumes the form:

$$\left|\frac{dw}{dz}\right| \leqslant \frac{1 - |w|^2}{1 - |z|^2}, \qquad (4\text{-}43)$$

or

$$|f'(z)| \leqslant \frac{1 - |f(z)|^2}{1 - |z|^2}. \qquad (4\text{-}44)$$

In fact, it is known that (4-44) holds without the restriction that $f(z)$ be univalent; it suffices to assume merely that $f(z)$ is analytic in the unit disc and that $|f(z)| < 1$ holds everywhere in the disc.

Nevertheless, the proof presented here has the feature of possessing a simple geometrical interpretation, which makes the correctness of (4-44) immediately evident without computation.

¶ 4-15 We conclude this chapter with an application of the concept of invariant length to the conformal mapping of doubly connected domains.

We begin by recalling the theorem that every doubly connected domain D can be mapped conformally onto any circular annulus whose inner and outer radii possess a ratio determined by D—i.e., if we consider all annuli with center at the origin and with outer radius equal to unity, then there is a *unique* annulus $\tilde{D}$ in this collection which is the conformal image of D. (We disregard the extreme cases in which one or both boundary components of D degenerate to a single point, for these are quite trivial and can be handled separately.) Furthermore, since the only conformal mappings of an annulus, defined by the inequalities $0 < R < |z| < 1$, onto itself are given by the equations $w = \gamma z$ and $w = \gamma R/z$, where $|\gamma| = 1$, it follows that there is much less arbitrariness in the mapping function than in the simply connected case. Indeed, if $w = f(z)$ furnishes one particular mapping of D onto $\tilde{D}$, then the only conformal mappings of D onto $\tilde{D}$ are of the form $w = \gamma f(z)$ and $w = \gamma R/f(z)$. Thus, given a point t of D, the set of all its possible images consists of precisely two circles (one circle in case $|f(t)| = R^{1/2}$) —namely, $|w| = |f(t)|$ and $|w| = R/|f(\theta)|$.

Two questions arise quite naturally: (a) Given D, how can R be determined? (b) Once R is known, how can a conformal mapping of D onto the annulus $R < |w| < 1$ (and, by the remarks made in the preceding paragraph, *all* conformal mappings of D onto the annulus $R < |w| < 1$) be determined?

Temporarily disregarding the domain D altogether, let us consider an annulus $\tilde{D}$ defined by the inequalities $R < |z| < 1$, and let us consider the space $\mathscr{L}_2(D)$. Since $\tilde{D}$, as explained above, can be mapped conformally onto itself in such a manner that points t and τ may be made to correspond whenever $|t| = |\tau|$ or $|t| = R/|\tau|$, it follows that the Gaussian curvature (or any other conformally invariant quantity) associated with the metric $K(z, z)\,|dz|^2$ must assume constant values along each circle $|z| = $ constant, and that the constant values associated with the pair of circles $|z| = \alpha$ and $|z| = R/\alpha$ must coincide. Thus, the curvature may be expressed as a function $C(|z|, R)$, where $C(|z|, R) = C(R/|z|, R)$. Similarly, instead of considering the metric $K(z, z) |dz|^2$ associated with the space $\mathscr{L}_2(D)$, we may consider the metric $K^{(s)}(z, z) |dz|^2$ associated with the subspace $\mathscr{L}_{2,s}(D)$ consisting of functions possessing single valued integrals, and we may then define a function $C_{(s)}(|z|, R)$ entirely analogous to $C(|z|, R)$. Now, a detailed computation, which will be sketched later in this section, shows that for each fixed value of R, the quantity $C_{(s)}(|z|, R)$ increases monotonely from the value -4π as $|z|$ increases from R to $R^{1/2}$, and then, of course, decreases monotonely to -4π as $|z|$ increases from $R^{1/2}$ to unity.* Furthermore, the maximum value of $C_{(s)}(|z|, R)$—namely $C_{(s)}(R^{1/2}, R)$—is itself a monotone function of R. Thus, the value of R, the inner radius of $\tilde{D}$, can be "recovered" from a knowledge of the curvature $C_{(s)}$ throughout $\tilde{D}$. Since $C_{(s)}$ is, aside from the inessential factor -2, equal to $(\lambda_{(s)}{}^1)^2/\lambda_{(s)}{}^{01}$, it follows that R can be found by computing the extremal quantities $\lambda_{(s)}{}^1$ and $\lambda_{(s)}{}^{01}$ throughout $\tilde{D}$.

Although this last remark may seem rather pointless, since $\tilde{D}$, and hence R, are assumed to be given, we may now make the following application of this remark. Suppose that a doubly connected domain D that is *not* an annulus is given, and suppose that we are able to determine $\lambda_{(s)}{}^1$ and $\lambda_{(s)}{}^{01}$, and hence $C_{(s)}$, everywhere in D. Taking account of the conformal invariance of $C_{(s)}$, it follows that the maximum value of $C_{(s)}$ must coincide with the quantity $C_{(s)}(R^{1/2}, R)$ associated with the *unique* annulus $\tilde{D}$ which is conformally equivalent to D. It now follows that from a knowledge of $C_{(s)}$ everywhere in D it is possible to *determine* the value of R associated with the conformally equivalent annulus $\tilde{D}$. Furthermore, each level curve Γ of $C_{(s)}$ in D must correspond to one of the two circles† in $\tilde{D}$ on which $C_{(s)}(|z|, R)$ has the same constant value as $C_{(s)}$ has on Γ. Also, the orthogonal trajectories of the level curves Γ must, by conformality, map onto the radial segments of $\tilde{D}$. Thus, it is evident how the equivalent annulus $\tilde{D}$ can be determined and how the conformal mapping of D onto $\tilde{D}$ can be effectively computed if the extremal quantities $\lambda_{(s)}{}^1$ and $\lambda_{(s)}{}^{01}$ can be determined everywhere in D.

It should be emphasized that the curvature associated with the kernel $K^{(s)}(z, z)$, rather than the one associated with the kernel

---

* It is seen without difficulty that the proof in Section 4-13 concerning the behavior of the curvature C near the boundary applies equally well to the curvature $C_{(s)}$ associated with the metric $K^{(s)}(z, z) |dz|^2$.

† The aforementioned exception concerning the circle of radius $R^{1/2}$ must be made.

$K(z, z)$, was employed in the above discussion. This was done because the monotonicity properties of the former curvature, which are *not* shared by the latter, make it quite obvious how the quantity R can be determined and the conformal mapping of D onto $\tilde{D}$ computed. It is evident, furthermore, that any conformally invariant quantity possessing suitable monotonicity properties may be employed in place of $C_{(s)}$. Actually, it is not difficult to see that knowledge of the behavior of *any* conformally invariant function that is not constant in the neighborhood of any point of D may furnish at least partial (and perhaps complete) information concerning the appropriate value of R and the nature of the function mapping D onto $\tilde{D}$, even when monotonicity properties similar to those possessed by $C_{(s)}(|z|, R)$ are lacking. We also remark that the same idea may be used in studying the mapping of domains of higher connectivity onto "canonical domains." Unfortunately, the actual determination of the kernels associated with such domains appears, at least until the present time, to be a task of great, perhaps insuperable, difficulty.

It remains to indicate how one establishes the properties of the curvature $C_{(s)}(|z|, R)$ which were employed in the foregoing discussion. For any fixed point t of the domain $\tilde{D}$ it is evident, by Laurent's theorem, that the kernel $K(z, t)$ can be expressed in the form:

$$K(z, t) = \sum_{n=-\infty}^{\infty} c_n(t)z^n, \quad R < |z| < 1. \tag{4-45}$$

In complete analogy with the manner in which we determined the kernel function of the unit disc in Section 3-2, we easily find that

$$t^n = \int\int_{\tilde{D}} z^n \overline{c_n(t)z^n} \, dx \, dy, \tag{4-46}$$

and so

$$\overline{c_n(t)} \equiv t^n \left(\int\int_{\tilde{D}} |z|^{2n} \, dx \, dy \right)^{-1}. \tag{4-47}$$

Now, a simple computation shows that

$$\int\int_{\tilde{D}} z^{2n} \, dx \, dy = \begin{cases} \dfrac{\pi}{n+1}(1 - R^{2n+2}), & n \neq -1, \\[2mm] -2\pi \log R, & n = -1. \end{cases} \tag{4-48}$$

We thus obtain the expansion

$$K(z, t) = \frac{1}{-2\pi z\bar{t} \log R} + \sum_{n \neq -1} \frac{n+1}{\pi(1 - R^{2n+2})} (z\bar{t})^n. \tag{4-49}$$

The same argument applies equally well to the determination of $K^{(s)}(z, t)$, except that the quantity $c_{-1}(t)$ must be assigned the value 0, for otherwise the kernel would not possess a single valued integral. Thus, we obtain the expansion

$$K^{(s)}(z, t) = \sum_{n \neq -1} \frac{n + 1}{\pi(1 - R^{2n+2})} (z\bar{t})^n. \tag{4-50}$$

Now, the functions $K(z, t)$ and $K^{(s)}(z, t)$ are closely related to the Weierstrass $\wp$–function, which plays a fundamental role in the theory of elliptic functions. The precise relationships are the following:

$$K(z, t) = \frac{1}{\pi z \bar{t}} \left[\wp (\log z\bar{t}; \omega_1, \omega_2) + \frac{\eta_1}{\pi i} - (2 \log R)^{-1} \right] \tag{4-51a}$$

$$K^{(s)}(z, t) = K(z, t) + (2\pi z\bar{t} \log R)^{-1}, \tag{4-51b}$$

where the fundamental period pair ω_1, ω_2 may be taken as $2\pi i$ and $-2 \log R$, respectively, and η_1 denotes the value of the integral $\int_{\zeta_1}^{\zeta_1 + 2\pi i} \wp(\zeta; \omega_1, \omega_2) \, d\zeta$ taken along any path that connects the points ζ_1 and $\zeta_1 + 2\pi i$ without passing through any of the poles of the integrand (which are located at all the integral linear combinations of ω_1 and ω_2). (Of course, ζ_1 must itself be a regular point of the integrand.) Identifying z and t, we immediately obtain explicit expressions for the invariant metrics $K(z, z) |dz|^2$ and $K^{(s)}(z, z) |dz|^2$, and then by straightforward but somewhat tedious computations the curvatures $C(|z|, R)$ and $C_{(s)}(|z|, R)$ are calculated. Finally, a rather careful and detailed analysis of the expressions thus obtained for the two curvatures shows that $C_{(s)}(|z|, R)$ possesses the monotonicity properties described earlier in this section, whereas $C(|z|, R)$ does not.

5

Generalizations of the Kernel Function

¶ **5-1** In this final chapter we shall attempt to indicate briefly how the concept of the reproducing kernel has been generalized in several directions.

First, we shall consider analytic functions of *two* complex variables. Given a domain D in the space of the complex variables z_1 ($= x_1 + iy_1$) and z_2 ($= x_2 + iy_2$), we consider the class $\mathscr{L}_2(D)$ of all functions $f(z_1, z_2)$ that are analytic* throughout D and that possess a finite quadratic integral $\iiiint_D |f|^2 \, dx_1 \, dy_1 \, dx_2 \, dy_2$. In complete analogy with the developments of earlier chapters, we can define the inner product

$$(f, g) = \iiiint_D f\bar{g} \, dx_1 \, dy_1 \, dx_2 \, dy_2 \tag{5-1}$$

---

* A function $f(z_1, z_2)$ is analytic at the point (t_1, t_2) if, in some neighborhood of this point, $f(z_1, z_2)$ is expressible as the sum of a power series $\sum\limits_{m,n=0}^{\infty} c_{mn}(z_1 - t_1)^m(z_2 - t_2)^n$.

and then, with the aid of a straightforward generalization* of (1-4), we can establish the completeness of $\mathscr{L}_2(D)$. Thus, we deduce the existence of a reproducing kernel $K(z_1, z_2; t_1, t_2)$ which is uniquely characterized [within the family $\mathscr{L}_2(D)$] by the obvious analogue of (3-3)—namely

$$f(t_1, t_2) = \iiiint_D f(z_1, z_2)\overline{K(z_1, z_2; t_1, t_2)}\, dx_1\, dy_1\, dx_2\, dy_2. \qquad (5\text{-}2)$$

The problem of minimizing $\|f\|^2$ among all functions in $\mathscr{L}_2(D)$ satisfying the condition $f(t_1, t_2) = 1$ possesses the unique solution $f(z_1, z_2) = K(z_1, z_2; t_1, t_2)/K(t_1, t_2; t_1, t_2)$, and the minimum value of $\|f\|^2$ is, of course, equal to $1/K(t_1, t_2; t_1, t_2)$. A "preferred" orthogonal basis may be associated with each point (t_1, t_2) of D, in analogy with the development presented in Section 3-6, and an expansion similar to (3-21) holds for the kernel. The method described in Section 3-7 for solving certain extremal problems by elementary considerations of a purely algebraic nature extends to the present case without any complication.

On the other hand, the definition of an invariant length analogous to (4-29) is not immediately evident. In the present case one seeks a positive definite† quadratic form in the differentials dx_1, dy_1, dx_2, dy_2 that is invariant under a one-to-one change of independent variables defined by means of a pair of analytic functions:

$$\zeta_1 = g_1(z_1, z_2), \qquad \zeta_2 = g_2(z_1, z_2). \qquad (5\text{-}3)$$

(Such a transformation is termed "pseudo-conformal," but it should be stressed that angles between curves are, in general, *not* preserved—in contrast with the case of one independent variable.) Such a differential form, which may be used to define a Riemannian geometry on equivalence classes of domains (in analogy with Section 4-9), is obtained by the following method:

Let a point (t_1, t_2) be selected in D and let us minimize $\|f\|^2$ among all functions in $\mathscr{L}_2(D)$ that satisfy the interpolation conditions

$$f(t_1, t_2) = 0, \qquad \alpha_1 f_{z_1}(t_1, t_2) + \alpha_2 f_{z_2}(t_1, t_2) = 1, \qquad (5\text{-}4)$$

---

* It is readily proved that the real and imaginary parts of an analytic function are harmonic functions of the four real variables x_1, y_1, x_2, y_2. From the mean value theorem for harmonic functions, which holds in any number of dimensions, it follows that $f^2(t_1, t_2)$ is equal to the mean value of $f^2(z_1, z_2)$ over the "volume" of any "sphere" with center at (t_1, t_2) which is contained entirely in D; from this equality one gets the desired inequality, exactly as in Chapter 1.

† I.e., assuming positive values except when $dx_1 = dy_2 = dx_2 = dy_2 = 0$.

where α_1 and α_2 are given constants that do not both vanish. By imitating suitably the arguments employed in Section 3-7, we find that the minimum of $\|f\|^2$ is equal to

$$\left(K \sum_{i,j=1}^{2} T_{ij}\alpha_i\bar{\alpha}_j\right)^{-1}, \tag{5-5}$$

where $K = K(t_1, t_2; t_1, t_2)$ and

$$T_{ij} = T_{ij}(t_1, t_2) = \frac{\partial^2 \log K(z_1, z_2; z_1, z_2)}{\partial z_i \, \partial \bar{z}_j}\bigg]_{z_1 = t_1, \, z_2 = t_2} \tag{5-6}$$

Since the expression (5-5) must necessarily be positive, it follows that the differential form

$$(ds)^2 = \sum_{i,j=1}^{2} T_{ij}(z_1, z_2) \, dz_i \, \overline{dz_j} \tag{5-7}$$

(which can evidently also be written as a form in the *real* differentials dx_1, dy_1, dx_2, dy_2) is positive definite. To demonstrate that the Riemannian metric (5-7) is invariant under the pseudo-conformal transformation (5-3), we write the transformation formula [entirely analogous to (4-29), both in content and in proof]:

$$K_D(z_1, z_2; z_1, z_2) = K_{\bar{D}}(\zeta_1, \zeta_2; \zeta_1, \zeta_2)|J|^2, \tag{5-8}$$

where J denotes the Jacobian of the transformation (5-3)—namely

$$J = \frac{\partial\zeta_1}{\partial z_1}\frac{\partial\zeta_2}{\partial z_2} - \frac{\partial\zeta_1}{\partial z_2}\frac{\partial\zeta_2}{\partial z_1}. \tag{5-9}$$

Taking the logarithm* of both sides of (5-8), we obtain

$$\log K_D(z_1, z_2; z_1, z_2) = \log K_{\bar{D}}(\zeta_1, \zeta_2; \zeta_1, \zeta_2) + \log J + \log \bar{J}. \tag{5-10}$$

Differentiating with respect to z_i and $\bar{z}_j$ and noting that

$$\partial^2 \log J/\partial z_i \, \partial \bar{z}_j \quad \text{and} \quad \partial^2 \log \bar{J}/\partial z_i \, \partial \bar{z}_j$$

must vanish [since $(\partial \log J)/(\partial \bar{z}_j) = (\partial \log \bar{J})/(\partial z_i) \equiv 0$], we obtain

$$\frac{\partial^2 \log K_D}{\partial z_i \, \partial \bar{z}_j} = \frac{\partial^2 \log K_{\bar{D}}}{\partial z_i \, \partial \bar{z}_j} = \sum_{k,m=1}^{2} \frac{\partial^2 \log K_{\bar{D}}}{\partial \zeta_k \, \partial \bar{\zeta}_m} \frac{\partial \zeta_k}{\partial z_i} \frac{\overline{\partial \zeta_m}}{\partial z_j}. \tag{5-11}$$

---

* Note that both sides of (5-8) are positive quantities; however, we find it convenient in the following argument to employ the logarithms of the complex quantity J and its conjugate $\bar{J}$.

Defining, in analogy with (5-6),

$$\tilde{T}_{km} = \frac{\partial^2 \log K_{\tilde{D}}(\zeta_1, \zeta_2; \bar{\zeta}_1, \bar{\zeta}_2)}{\partial \zeta_k \, \partial \bar{\zeta}_m}, \tag{5-12}$$

we observe that (5-11) may be rewritten in the form

$$T_{ij} = \sum_{k,m=1}^{2} \tilde{T}_{km} \frac{\partial \zeta_k}{\partial z_i} \overline{\frac{\partial \zeta_m}{\partial z_j}}, \tag{5-13}$$

and it is then easily shown that

$$\sum_{i,j=1}^{2} T_{ij} \, dz_i \, \overline{dz_j} = \sum_{k,m=1}^{2} \tilde{T}_{k1} \, d\zeta_k \, \overline{d\zeta_1}. \tag{5-14}$$

The invariance of the Riemannian metric (5-7) under pseudo-conformal mapping is thus established.

Now, let any two domains D and $\tilde{D}$ be given that possess the same topological structure. It is natural to seek to determine whether D and $\tilde{D}$ are pseudo-conformally equivalent—i.e., whether there exists a pair of functions $g_1(z_1, z_2)$, $g_2(z_1, z_2)$ that are analytic in D and map D onto $\tilde{D}$ in a one-to-one manner. If in any way a scalar function S is defined in each domain, and if it can be shown that S must remain unaltered by pseudo-conformal transformation, it follows that if D and $\tilde{D}$ are pseudo-conformally equivalent, the "level surfaces" $S = $ constant in D and $\tilde{D}$ must be mapped onto each other by the transformation. (This same idea has been discussed in Section 4-15.) In particular, if S reduces to a constant in one domain and to a different constant, or to a nonconstant function, in the other domain, then the two domains cannot be pseudo-conformally equivalent. As an illustration, let us consider the scalar function

$$S = \frac{T_{11}T_{22} - T_{12}T_{21}}{K(z_1, z_2; \bar{z}_1, \bar{z}_2)}. \tag{5-15}$$

It is easily shown, with the aid of (5-8) and (5-13), that this function is pseudo-conformally invariant. Let the domain D be taken as the interior of the unit sphere—namely, the set of points defined by the inequality

$$|z_1|^2 + |z_2|^2 = x_1^2 + y_1^2 + x_2^2 + y_2^2 < 1, \tag{5-16}$$

and let $\tilde{D}$ be taken as the "unit bi-cylinder," defined by the inequalities

$$|z_1| < 1 \qquad |z_2| < 1. \tag{5-17}$$

Now, by imitating rather closely the argument employed in Section 3-2, we obtain for the kernels of D and $\tilde{D}$ the following expressions:*

$$K_D(z_1, z_2; t_1, t_2) = \frac{2}{\pi^2(1 - z_1\bar{t}_1 - z_2\bar{t}_2)^3}, \qquad (5\text{-}18a)$$

$$K_{\tilde{D}}(z_1, z_2; t_1, t_2) = \frac{1}{\pi^2(1 - z_1\bar{t}_1)^2(1 - z_2\bar{t}_2)^2}. \qquad (5\text{-}18b)$$

Straightforward computations now furnish for the scalar invariant S the following results:

$$S \equiv \frac{9\pi^2}{2} \text{ in } D, \qquad S \equiv 4\pi^2 \text{ in } \tilde{D}. \qquad (5\text{-}19)$$

This result establishes the fact that the sphere and bi-cylinder are not pseudo-conformally equivalent, contrary to what might be expected. Thus, there is no immediate generalization of the Riemann mapping theorem to the theory of pseudo-conformal mapping.

PROBLEM

    5-1. Demonstrate that the function S defined by (5-15) is pseudo-conformally invariant.

¶ **5-2** In this section we shall establish a close relationship between the reproducing kernel of a plane domain D and another very important function associated with D—namely the Green's function. This function, which we shall denote $G(z, t)$, is defined as follows: For a fixed point t in D, $G(z, t)$ is a harmonic function of z everywhere in D except at t; $G(z, t) + \log |z - t|$ remains harmonic at t; and $G(z, t)$ approaches 0 as z approaches any boundary point of D. Under very general hypotheses on the boundary of D the existence (and uniqueness) of the Green's function is assured, and under suitable additional hypotheses on the smoothness of the boundary, which we assume to be satisfied, the Green's function possesses sufficient differentiability properties on the boundary—i.e., for z on the boundary—to justify the computations that will be carried out. For example, it suffices to assume that the boundary of D consists of

---

* Formula (5-18b) illustrates the following theorem, which we do not prove here: If the domain D is the Cartesian product of plane domains D_1 and D_2—i.e., if D consists of those points (z_1, z_2) that satisfy the conditions $z_1 \in D_1$, $z_2 \in D_2$—then $K_D(z_1, z_2; t_1, t_2) = K_{D_1}(z_1, t_1)K_{D_2}(z_2, t_2)$.

a finite number of simple closed curves possessing continuous curvature—i.e., each curve possesses finite length and can be parametrized in terms of the arc-length by equations $x = f(s)$, $y = g(s)$, where the second derivatives $f''(s)$ and $g''(s)$ exist and are continuous.

Let $f(z)$ be analytic in D and continuous in $\bar{D}$. Then, if t is chosen anywhere in D, we may express $f(t)$ in accordance with the Cauchy integral formula:

$$f(t) = \frac{1}{2\pi i} \int_\Gamma \frac{f(z)}{z - t} dz. \qquad (5\text{-}20)$$

(Γ, of course, denotes the boundary of D.) According to the definition of $G(z, t)$, we may write

$$G(z, t) = \tfrac{1}{2} \log (z - t) + \tfrac{1}{2} \log \overline{(z - t)} + H(z, t), \qquad (5\text{-}21)$$

where $H(z, t)$, considered as a function of z, is harmonic everywhere in D, including t. Differentiating (5-21) with respect to t, we obtain

$$\frac{1}{z - t} = -2G_t(z, t) + 2H_t(z, t). \qquad (5\text{-}22)$$

Since G, as a function of z, vanishes identically on Γ, the first term on the right side of (5-22) must also vanish as z describes Γ, and so (5-20) may be rewritten in the form

$$f(t) = -\frac{1}{\pi i} \int_\Gamma f(z) H_t \, dz \qquad (5\text{-}23)$$

or

$$\frac{i}{2} \int_\Gamma f(z) H_t \, dz = \frac{\pi}{2} f(t). \qquad (5\text{-}24)$$

By Stokes' theorem (see Appendix), we obtain

$$\frac{\pi}{2} f(t) = -\int\int_D (fH_t)_{\bar{z}} \, dx \, dy. \qquad (5\text{-}25)$$

Since f is analytic in z and $H(z, t)$ is real valued, it is easily seen that we may rewrite (5-25) in the form

$$f(t) = -\frac{2}{\pi} \int\int_D f(z) \overline{H_{zt}} \, dx \, dy. \qquad (5\text{-}26)$$

Now, by referring to (5-21) we find that H_{zt} is the same as G_{zt}, and so we obtain

$$f(t) = \int\int_{\bar{D}} f(z) \overline{\left(-\frac{2}{\pi} G_{zt}\right)} \, dx \, dy. \qquad (5\text{-}27)$$

Next, by suitable approximation arguments, (5-27) can be established under the hypothesis that $f(z)$ belongs to $\mathscr{L}_2(D)$—i.e., the requirement that $f(z)$ remain continuous on Γ may be dropped. Then, by comparing (5-27) with (3-3) and recalling that $K(z, t)$ is uniquely determined within $\mathscr{L}_2(D)$ by its reproducing property, we obtain the remarkable identity

$$K(z, t) = -\frac{2}{\pi} G_{z\bar{t}}(z, t). \tag{5-28}$$

To illustrate (5-28), we take D as the unit disc, in which case it is well known (and easily confirmed) that

$$G(z, t) = \log \left| \frac{1 - z\bar{t}}{z - t} \right|. \tag{5-29}$$

For convenience we rewrite (5-29) in the form

$$G(z, t) = \tfrac{1}{2} \log (1 - z\bar{t}) + \tfrac{1}{2} \log (1 - \bar{z}t)$$
$$- \tfrac{1}{2} \log (z - t) - \tfrac{1}{2} \log (\bar{z} - \bar{t}). \tag{5-30}$$

From (5-30) we immediately obtain

$$G_{z\bar{t}}(z, t) = -\frac{1}{2(1 - z\bar{t})^2}, \tag{5-31}$$

and now by substituting into (5-28) we obtain

$$K(z, t) = \frac{1}{\pi(1 - z\bar{t})^2} \tag{5-32}$$

in agreement with (3-12).

PROBLEM

5-2. Prove the correctness of (5-28) for a simply connected domain D by showing that if (5-28) is correct for the unit disc, it is correct for D. (The idea is basically the same as that employed in Section 4-5.)

¶ **5-3** We conclude our brief discussion of generalizations of the reproducing kernel by considering kernels associated with families of harmonic, rather than of analytic, functions.

A rather obvious extension of the ideas presented in the initial chapters is to replace the class of functions analytic and quadratically integrable over the plane domain D by the class of all (real-valued) functions that are harmonic and quadratically integrable over D. These functions obviously form a linear space (over the real field), and a real-valued inner product may be defined in the obvious manner—namely

$$(u, v) = \iint_D uv \, dx \, dy. \tag{5-33}$$

Although the analytic function $f(z)$ cannot be replaced in (1-1) by the harmonic function $u(x, y)$ (since the square of a real-valued harmonic function is not harmonic, except in the trivial case of constant functions), we may nevertheless establish the analogues of (1-3) and (1-4) by the following argument. Since u is harmonic, it possesses the "areal" mean-value property—namely

$$\pi R^2 u(t) = \iint\limits_{|z-t| < R} u(z) \, dx \, dy. \tag{5-34}$$

By the Schwarz inequality for integrals we then obtain

$$(\pi R^2 u(t))^2 \leqslant \left(\iint\limits_{|z-t| < R} 1^2 \, dx \, dy \right) \left(\iint\limits_{|z-t| < R} u^2(z) \, dx \, dy \right), \tag{5-35}$$

which simplifies to

$$\pi R^2 u^2(t) \leqslant \iint\limits_{|z-t| < R} u^2(z) \, dx \, dy. \tag{5-36}$$

From this we immediately obtain, in complete analogy with (1-3),

$$\pi R^2 u^2(t) \leqslant \iint_D u^2 \, dx \, dy = \|u\|^2. \tag{5-37}$$

It is now apparent that the convergence theory developed in Chapter 1 and the proofs presented in Chapter 3 of the existence of a reproducing kernel and of the bilinear expansion (3-20) apply equally well to the class of functions now under consideration. We also observe that, since the mean-value theorem holds for harmonic functions of any number of variables, the entire theory applies equally well to domains in higher-dimensional spaces.

More interesting and significant results are obtained, however, by employing a different inner product. Returning to the two-dimensional case for ease in exposition (although the ideas are again applicable in higher dimensions), let us consider all functions harmonic in a bounded domain whose boundary Γ consists of a finite number of simple closed curves that are sufficiently smooth to justify the steps that follow. From among these functions we select those that remain continuous on the boundary of D, satisfy the "boundary condition"

$$\int_\Gamma u \, ds = 0, \tag{5-38}$$

and possess a finite Dirichlet integral

$$D(u) = \iint_D (u_x{}^2 + u_y{}^2) \, dx \, dy. \tag{5-39}$$

It is evident that this class of functions constitutes a vector space, and that an inner product may be defined by

$$(u, v) = \iint_D (u_x v_x + u_y v_y) \, dx \, dy. \tag{5-40}$$

(The condition (5-38) is introduced in order to assure that only the zero function has zero norm, rather than all *constant* functions.) However, the inner-product space so defined may not be complete, for reasons that will be explained later. Furthermore, it is not immediately evident that for the functions of this class an inequality of the form

$$|u(t)| \leqslant c(t)\|u\| \tag{5-41}$$

must hold, where $c(t)$, as in (1-4), denotes a quantity depending only on the point t (and the domain D) but not on the function u. Thus, it is not possible to assert immediately that a reproducing kernel analogous to that defined in Chapter 3 for the family of analytic functions $\mathscr{L}_2(D)$ must exist. Nevertheless, we shall *directly* demonstrate the existence of a reproducing kernel, and from this fact the existence of an inequality of the form (5-41) will be immediately evident. It will then be possible to show that the family of harmonic functions under consideration may be so enlarged, by modifying suitably the condition (5-38), that it becomes a Hilbert space [with the inner product (5-40)].

The Neumann's function $N(z, t)$ associated with the domain D is defined, in close analogy with the Green's function (cf. Section 5-2), as follows:

(a) For each point t of D, $N(z, t)$ is harmonic for all points z in D except t.

(b) $N(z, t) + \log |z - t|$ remains harmonic at t.

(c) The normal derivative $\partial N(z, t)/\partial n_z$ is constant everywhere on Γ; from this it follows by a simple computation that the constant value of this derivative must be equal to $-2\pi/L$,* where L denotes the length of Γ.

---

* The minus sign holds with the understanding that the *outward* normal is chosen.

(d) $\int_\Gamma N(z, t)\, ds$ vanishes for each point t; this condition serves to dispose of an arbitrary additive "constant" (actually, a function of t), which is allowed by conditions (a), (b), and (c). Now, in addition to the formula

$$u(t) = -\frac{1}{2\pi} \int_\Gamma u(z)\, \frac{\partial G}{\partial n}\, ds, \qquad (5\text{-}42a)$$

which holds for any function harmonic in D behaving suitably on Γ, but *not* necessarily satisfying the restriction (5-38), we can easily establish that when (5-38) *is* satisfied, the additional equality

$$0 = -\frac{1}{2\pi} \int_\Gamma u(z)\, \frac{\partial N}{\partial n}\, ds \qquad (5\text{-}42b)$$

holds everywhere in D. Subtracting these last two equations, we obtain

$$u(t) = \frac{1}{2\pi} \int_\Gamma u(z)\, \frac{\partial k}{\partial n}\, (z, t)\, ds, \qquad (5\text{-}43)$$

where

$$k(z, t) = \frac{1}{2\pi}\{N(z, t) - G(z, t)\}. \qquad (5\text{-}44)$$

Since $k(z, t)$ remains harmonic at t [on account of the cancellation of the singularities of $N(z, t)$ and $G(z, t)$], we may apply Green's identity to the right side of (5-43), obtaining

$$u(t) = \iint_D (u_x k_x + u_y k_y)\, dx\, dy, \qquad (5\text{-}45)$$

or, taking account of (5-40),

$$u(t) = (u(z), k(z, t)). \qquad (5\text{-}46)$$

Thus, the function $k(z, t)$ is, as suggested by the notation, a reproducing kernel in the inner-product space under consideration. By the Schwarz inequality (which holds in any inner-product space, not necessarily complete), we obtain*

$$|u(t)| \leqslant \|u\| \cdot \|k\| = (k(t, t))^{1/2} \|u\|. \qquad (5\text{-}47)$$

Now let us consider, in the inner-product space under consideration, a Cauchy sequence $\{u_n\}$. Replacing $u(t)$ in (5-47) by the difference of any two members of this sequence, we find that this sequence converges *pointwise* everywhere in D; furthermore, the continuity

---

* The equality in (5-47) is obtained by replacing $u(z)$ in (5-46) by $k(z, t)$.

of $k(t, t)^*$ enables us to assert that the convergence is *uniform* on every compact subset of D. By suitably imitating the reasoning employed in Section 1-4, we conclude that the limit function, which we momentarily denote as u, possesses a finite Dirichlet integral (5-39) and that $\|u - u_n\| \to 0$, so that u is the limit-in-norm, as well as the pointwise limit, of the given sequence of functions. (On the other hand, the condition (5-38) may very well be meaningless, for the function u may not remain continuous up to the boundary.) It is then easy to show that (5-46) holds for the limit function u, and that the space $\mathscr{D}_2(D)$, consisting of the functions originally introduced—i.e., those satisfying (5-38)—*together with* the limits of their Cauchy sequences, *is* complete. Thus, the function $k(z, t)$ defined by (5-44) constitutes a reproducing kernel in the Hilbert space $\mathscr{D}_2(D)$, and it is readily seen that it admits a bilinear expansion, completely analogous to (3-20), in terms of any complete orthonormal set of functions.

A particularly interesting application of the reproducing kernel $k(z, t)$ is to the solution of the Dirichlet problem. As is well known, this is the problem of constructing a (necessarily unique) function that is harmonic in the domain D, continuous in $\bar{D}$, and that coincides on the boundary of D with a specified continuous function f. This problem is always solvable if the boundary satisfies certain mild conditions, and under more stringent conditions is expressible in terms of the Green's function $G(z, t)$ as follows:

$$u(t) = -\frac{1}{2\pi} \int_\Gamma f \frac{\partial G}{\partial n}(z, t)\, ds. \qquad (5\text{-}48)$$

Taking account of (5-44) and the definition of the Neumann's function $N(z, t)$, we obtain

$$u(t) = \int_\Gamma f \frac{\partial k}{\partial n}\, ds + \frac{1}{L} \int_\Gamma f\, ds. \qquad (5\text{-}49)$$

[In (5-48) and (5-49), as previously, Γ denotes the boundary of D, and $\partial/\partial n$ denotes differentiation in the direction of the outward normal.]

Similarly, the solution to the Neumann problem—namely, to determine a function v harmonic in D and possessing a normal

---

* The functions $G(z, t) + \log|z - t|$ and $N(z, t) + \log|z - t|$, and hence the function $k(z, t)$, are continuous in both variables.

derivative $\partial v/\partial n$ that agrees with a specified function h defined on Γ (subject to the restrictions* $\int_\Gamma v \, ds = 0, \int_\Gamma h \, ds = 0$)—is furnished by the formula

$$v(t) = -\frac{1}{2\pi} \int_\Gamma hN(z, t) \, ds. \qquad (5\text{-}50)$$

Now, since $G(z, t)$ vanishes when z is on Γ, (5-50) may be rewritten in the form

$$v(t) = -\int_\Gamma hk(z, t) \, ds. \qquad (5\text{-}51)$$

Thus, we see that both the Dirichlet and Neumann problems (for a domain with sufficiently smooth boundary) are solvable with the aid of the *single* domain function $k(z, t)$, whereas the more classical formulas (5-48) and (5-50) involve the *distinct* domain functions $G(z, t)$ and $N(z, t)$.

In conclusion, we shall compute explicitly the kernel $k(z, t)$ for the unit disc and, by combining our result with the well-known formula for the Green's function of this domain, obtain an explicit formula for the Neumann's function $N(z, t)$. From the elements of potential theory it is known that any function $v(z)$ harmonic in the unit disc is expressible in the form

$$v(z) = \tfrac{1}{2}a_0 + \sum_{n=1}^{\infty} r^n(a_n \cos n\theta + b_n \sin n\theta), \quad z = re^{i\theta}. \qquad (5\text{-}52)$$

Identifying $v(z)$ with $k(z, t)$ and taking account of (5-38), we immediately observe that a_0 must vanish, whereas the remaining coefficients a_n and b_n (which, of course, depend on t) are determined as follows. By an elementary computation based on Green's theorem we easily show that each of the functions $r \cos \theta$, $r \sin \theta$, $r^2 \cos 2\theta$, $r^2 \sin 2\theta, \ldots$ is orthogonal [with the definition (5-40) of the inner product] to every other function in this collection. Hence, replacing $u(z)$ in (5-46) by $r^m \cos m\theta$, we obtain

$$\rho^m \cos m\alpha = (r^m \cos m\theta, a_m r^m \cos m\theta), \quad t = \rho e^{i\alpha}, \qquad (5\text{-}53)$$

and from this we obtain, by a simple computation,

$$a_m = (\pi m)^{-1} \rho^m \cos m\alpha. \qquad (5\text{-}54)$$

---

* The first of these conditions is introduced to eliminate an arbitrary additive constant [cf. (5-38)], and the second condition must be satisfied by the normal derivative of any function harmonic in the domain D.

Similarly,
$$b_m = (\pi m)^{-1} \rho^m \sin m\alpha, \qquad (5\text{-}55)$$

and now we obtain, by substituting from (5-54) and (5-55) into (5-52):
$$k(z, t) = \sum_{n=1}^{\infty} (\pi n)^{-1}(r\rho)^n \cos n(\theta - \alpha). \qquad (5\text{-}56)$$

This series constitutes the real part of the series
$$\sum_{n=1}^{\infty} (\pi n)^{-1} w^n, \quad w = r\rho e^{i(\theta - \alpha)},$$

whose sum is equal to $-\pi^{-1} \log (1 - w)$. Thus, we obtain
$$k(z, t) = -\pi^{-1} \log |1 - r\rho e^{i(\theta - \alpha)}|, \qquad (5\text{-}57)$$

or, more explicitly,
$$k(z, t) = -\frac{1}{2\pi} \log (1 - 2r\rho \cos (\theta - \alpha) + r^2\rho^2). \qquad (5\text{-}58)$$

Taking account of (5-58), (5-44), and the familiar formula
$$G(z, t) = \tfrac{1}{2} \log \frac{1 - 2r\rho \cos (\theta - \alpha) + r^2\rho^2}{r^2 - 2r\rho \cos (\theta - \alpha) + \rho^2}, \qquad (5\text{-}59)$$

we obtain for the Neumann's function the explicit formula
$$N(z, t) = -\tfrac{1}{2} \log [(1 - 2r\rho \cos (\theta - \alpha) + r^2\rho^2) \times (r^2 - 2r\rho \cos (\theta - \alpha) + \rho^2)]. \qquad (5\text{-}60)$$

APPENDIX and BIBLIOGRAPHY

Appendix

Complex Differentiation and Stokes' Theorem

¶ **A-1** Let $f(x, y)$ denote a complex-valued function defined in some neighborhood of the point (x_0, y_0). If the partial derivatives $f_x(x, y)$ and $f_y(x, y)$ exist at the point (x_0, y_0), we define the "complex derivatives" f_z and $f_{\bar{z}}$ as follows:

$$f_z = \tfrac{1}{2}(f_x - if_y), \qquad f_{\bar{z}} = \tfrac{1}{2}(f_x + if_y). \tag{A-1}$$

It is readily seen that the familiar rules for differentiating a sum, product, difference, and quotient continue to be valid. Furthermore, if $f(x, y)$ is analytic at the point z_0, then a simple computation (Problem A-1) shows that f_z coincides with the derivative $f'(z_0)$ as defined in the theory of analytic functions, whereas $f_{\bar{z}}$ vanishes. Conversely, if $f(x, y)$ is anti-analytic in a neighborhood of z_0—i.e., if $\overline{f(x, y)}$ is analytic in z—then f_z vanishes at z_0 and $f_{\bar{z}}$ equals the *conjugate* of $g'(z_0)$, where $g(z) = g(x, y) = \overline{f(x, y)}$.

In particular, if $f(z)$ and $h(z)$ are analytic in a domain D, then the equalities $(f\bar{h})_z = f'(z)\overline{h(z)}$ and $(f\bar{h})_{\bar{z}} = f(z)\overline{h'(z)}$ hold everywhere in D.

PROBLEMS

A-1. Prove that, if $f(x, y)$ is an analytic function of the complex variable $z\,(= x + iy)$ in a domain, then f_z coincides with the derivative $f'(z)$, whereas $f_{\bar{z}}$ vanishes. *Hint:* Use the definitions (A-1) in conjunction with the Cauchy-Riemann equations.

A-2. Let $f(x, y)$ possess continuous partial derivatives f_x and f_y in a domain D, and suppose that $f_{\bar{z}}$ vanishes identically in D. Prove that $f(z)$ is analytic in D.

A-3. Let $u(x, y)$ be harmonic in a domain D. Prove that u_z equals $\frac{1}{2}f'(z)$, where $f(z)$ is an analytic function whose real part is u.

A-4. Let $u(x, y)$ possess continuous second derivatives u_{xx}, $u_{xy}\,(= u_{yx})$, u_{yy} in a domain D. Prove that $(u_z)_{\bar{z}} = (u_{\bar{z}})_z = \frac{1}{4}(u_{xx} + u_{yy})$.

¶ **A-2** In this section we shall establish Stokes' theorem, which relates a certain area integral to an integral over the boundary, in a form particularly adapted to the case when analytic functions are involved. We recall that if u and v are sufficiently differentiable (real- or complex-valued) functions defined on a bounded domain D and its boundary Γ, which is assumed to consist of a finite number of sufficiently smooth curves, then

$$\iint_D \left(\frac{\partial u}{\partial x} + \frac{\partial v}{\partial y}\right) dx\,dy = \int_\Gamma u\,dy - v\,dx, \qquad \text{(A-2)}$$

where the integration over Γ is to be performed in the positive (counterclockwise) sense with respect to D. If $v \equiv iu$, then (A-2) assumes the form

$$\iint_D \left(\frac{\partial u}{\partial x} + i\frac{\partial u}{\partial y}\right) dx\,dy = -i\int_\Gamma u\,dz. \qquad \text{(A-3)}$$

Taking account of (A-1), we may also write (A-3) in the form

$$\iint_D u_{\bar{z}}\,dx\,dy = -\frac{i}{2}\int_\Gamma u\,dz. \qquad \text{(A-4)}$$

In particular, if $u = f(z)\overline{h(z)}$, where $f(z)$ and $h(z)$ are analytic in D (and suitably behaved on the boundary), we obtain the desired version of Stokes' theorem—namely

$$\iint_D f\overline{h'}\,dx\,dy = -\frac{i}{2}\int_\Gamma f\bar{h}\,dz. \qquad \text{(A-5)}$$

Bibliography

The following books contain extensive references to literature in the research journals:

1. S. Bergman, *Sur les fonctions orthogonales de plusieurs variables complexes avec les applications à la théorie des fonctions analytiques*, Memorial des Sciences Mathématiques, CVI, Paris, 1947.

2. S. Bergman, *Sur la fonction-noyau d'un domaine et ses applications dans la théorie des transformations pseudoconformes*, Mémorial des Sciences Mathématiques, CVII, Paris, 1948.

3. S. Bergman, *The Kernel Function and Conformal Mapping*, Mathematical Surveys, V, American Mathematical Society, New York, 1950.

4. S. Bergman and M. Schiffer, *Kernel Functions and Elliptic Differential Equations in Mathematical Physics*, Academic Press, New York, 1953.

5. H. Meschkowski, *Hilbertsche Räume mit Kernfunktion*, Springer-Verlag, Berlin, 1962.

INDEX